In Praise of
Let's Have Lunch Together

"This book made me re-think the way I do things with regard to boards and fundraising—not some more 'principles of fund development,' you gave me the how-tos. It's now required reading in our fundraising courses. As a professor of sociology, I review lots of textbooks. What a relief when I read *Let's Have Lunch Together*. Much more rich and applicable than a traditional textbook. Clear, concise, with identifiable characters."

Matthew A. Jendian, Ph.D.
Director, American Humanics Nonprofit Administration Program
California State University, Fresno

"Spending time with this book is the most fun I've ever had being trained. This learning novel approach to relationship-building is the best I've ever experienced. The story captured my heart, and then my mind, as it moved me along a process of self-discovery and ultimately to enlightenment. At first I resisted, then I realized, 'This is my story.' I finally got the 'Ah ha.' This is a resource that I will use over and over again for many years."

Tim Reese, Executive Director
California-Nevada Community Action Partnership

"As a major gift fundraiser of 16 years, I found this a transforming book. It presents the single most important lesson for major gift fundraising. Marshall Howard shows nonprofit leadership how to tap into their own individual strengths, talents, and potentials to create a stronger bond with current and future donors: to trust in their own personal ability. He shows how pressures and discomforts can be eliminated and how major gifts work doesn't have to feel like work at all. I thoroughly enjoyed reading it. Highly recommended."

Gary B. Grant
Director of Major Gifts
National Alzheimer's Association

"'Food for the Gods' for those who dare to master the power of strategic relationships. Exceptionally beneficial for the seasoned veteran, the novice fundraiser, and to empower board members. A must read for stalled or stymied growth. Kudos to Marshall Howard for removing the mystique, sharing the coveted secrets, and all the benefits of a powerful relationship through his simple, step-by-step, 'laptop references'—benefits which can also be applied to our personal daily lives."

DeNelle Ellison, Director
Marketing, Fund Development, and Special Events
Greater Sacramento Urban League

"I wish I had this book years ago as Vice President of Development at Inova Health Systems. It would have been required reading for both my staff as well as volunteers, management, and physicians who were involved with our Foundation to secure major gifts."

Steve Meyerson
Principal, Meyerson & Associates

"As a twenty-year fundraising veteran and a former regional vice president with the American Cancer Society, this is simply the best book on fundraising that I have ever read. Working with MH&A, I can say firsthand these steps and systems work!"

James Claitor, Principal
Momentum to Execution

"For the first time in nonprofit management, Marshall Howard makes relationships and the steps and skills needed to build them come alive. This novel is a great learning tool."

Kylie Schwerdtfeger, Program Director
The Green Foundation

"This little book is chock full of golden nuggets and highlighted nuances that make such a huge difference in building stronger relationships. As a former client of MH&A with Big Brothers Big Sisters, I made lots of miracles happen with this system."

Paul Oleniacz, Development Officer
Inland Northwest Blood Center

"This book is a must read for nonprofit leaders and fund development personnel. I immediately set about having our management team read it as well, including our Director of Volunteer Recruitment. The learning novel approach works and makes this a very easy and enjoyable read, while still underscoring the critical value of relationship-building."

Warren M. Grymes, Chief Executive Officer
Big Brothers Big Sisters of Northwest Florida

"An easy read, full of life experiences. This book helps make that important transition to being more successful in cultivating donor relationships. That's what empowers you to meet your objectives."

Richard George, President
Junior Achievement of West Central Florida, Inc.

"This book finally provides a step-by-step relationship-building system by an author and consultant with long and deep experience in delivering successful outcomes. Read it and take away the 'how to's.'"

Frank McIntosh, President
Junior Achievement of Delaware, Inc.

"If you don't have the opportunity to hear Marshall Howard speak, participate in one of his workshops, or engage his firm as we did, make this book your relationship-building Bible. He's the 'dean' of relationship-building."

Bob Olson, Vice President
Washoe Medical Foundation

Let's Have Lunch Together

A Learning Novel for Nonprofits by
MARSHALL HOWARD

Directed by Arthur Bauer

Kings Road Press

Attention nonprofit and professional organizations, universities, and corporations. Special quantity discounts are available for educational, training, and fundraising purposes. Special materials or book excerpts can also be created to fit specific needs.

For information, please contact:
Marshall Howard & Associates
22148 Sherman Way, Suite 202
Canoga Park, CA 91303
Phone: 818-340-9202, Fax: 818-340-0353, E-mail:
mhoward@marshallhoward.com
or visit our website at www.marshallhoward.com

A Kings Road Book
Published by Kings Road Press
A division of TCI
Printed and bound in the United States of America

Marshall Howard

Marshall Howard is President and CEO of two relationship-building companies he founded in the early 1980s: Marshall Howard & Associates and Golf West.

His wide-ranging background as an attorney, former television network executive, teacher, and sales and marketing consultant, led him to quickly discover why so many nonprofits have such difficulty increasing funding and getting more of what they want and need: lack of strong relationships with the right people.

Built on the belief that people and the strength of their relationships are one of the key sources of success, Marshall Howard has pioneered a groundbreaking, copyrighted program, "Relationship Builders." His step-by-step system demystifies the art of great relationship-building, removes the roadblocks, reveals the secrets, and delivers the how-tos. The essence of "Relationship Builders" comes alive in this book.

Marshall has shown thousands of nonprofit staff and volunteers throughout the country how they can raise millions of dollars, build influential boards, and expand their mission programs in record time, using the power of strong relationships.

Marshall Howard's successes and programs have been reported in the *Los Angeles Times*, *U.S. News & World Report*, *Sales & Marketing Management*, *Los Angeles Business Journal*, *Success Magazine*, and in many other businesses and fundraising publications.

Clients include a range of nonprofits big and small: Alegent Health Systems, American Cancer Society, American Red Cross, Big Brothers Big Sisters, Hope International University, Junior Achievement, San Francisco Zoological Society, SPCA, Teach for America, University of Judaism, YMCA, and hundreds of others.

Marshall continues to share his relationship-building tips and systems as a speaker and workshop facilitator at local meetings, regional and national conferences, and through board retreats, training seminars, and client consulting nationwide.

Arthur Bauer

Art Bauer is the founder and former president of American Media Incorporated, the largest soft skill video training company in the world. Before selling the firm, it grew to 2.5 times the size of its nearest competitor.

Art was a two-time finalist for the Entrepreneur of the Year Award by Ernst and Young. He has produced and directed more than 1,000 training films and videos and is co-owner of the business management icon film, Dr. Ken Blanchard's "The Story of a New One Minute Manager." Mr. Bauer has also authored numerous motivational and management books and CDs. He is the recipient of over 130 national and international awards for his works.

As a recognized consultant and speaker on management, selling, and motivation, Mr. Bauer has shared his experience and knowledge in seminars across the United States and throughout the world, including Africa, Europe, South America, and China.

Art Bauer's clients have included Boeing, Exxon, General Motors, Hilton Hotels, IBM, State Farm Insurance, Sears, UPS, and hundreds of other Fortune 1000 companies.

Acknowledgements

First, I extend my heartfelt thanks and deepest appreciation to Art Bauer, a friend and colleague for over 25 years. His guidance, coaching, and support helped to transform a dream into reality.

Thanks to all the staff of MH&A and Golf West for countless ideas and helping me re-live some of the client challenges and successes that are illustrated throughout the book.

And special thanks to the over 50 nonprofits, universities, board members, and volunteers who have helped me, each in their own way, to demystify a challenging fundraising area and to make the art of relationship-building come alive: American Cancer Society, Boys & Girls Clubs, California State University, Indiana University Center on Philanthropy, Volunteers of America, Vistacare Hospice Foundation, YWCA, and so many others.

Most importantly, thanks to my wife Dell, my daughter Stacie, and my son Brandon for your love and support throughout this journey.

Table of Contents

Introduction

Someone would have to live alone in a cave not to understand the importance of relationships or how to build and keep them, said Oscar to himself. This is a story, inspired by our clients, about a likeable, but somewhat stressed and overworked, Executive Director named Oscar. Although he knows relationships with the right people are critical to his organization and his fund development, he just can't figure out what more he can do, or what he can do differently, to make them stronger and work better!

From my thousands of conversations with nonprofits throughout the country over the past 24 years, one universal challenge stands out. Staff and supporters constantly struggle to secure more funding to grow and expand their great missions.

It's not that most nonprofits don't try or don't have the technology. Nor is it because of a lack of hard work, vision, dedicated staff, or deeply committed supporters.

I've discovered that most organizations operate year after year with a huge asset gap that holds them back—they don't have strong relationships with enough of the right people. Others can't comfortably turn the relationships they do have into fundraising successes.

A strong relationship is by far the most effective way to raise more money, reduce stress, and make work and life more rewarding and a lot more fun. Although most people understand the importance of relationships, I'm amazed at how much gets lost in the day-to-day execution.

I've watched hundreds of nonprofits endlessly search to uncover their silver bullet of fundraising. "If I could just get more effective donor software, build a better direct mail program, beef up grants, or add some exciting new events, things would be great." But the struggles continue and things don't change very much.

Most organizations already have most of the tools that they need to dramatically increase their income, except for one—strong relationships with the right people who have the capacity to make more miracles happen.

Regardless of how much money you want to raise or how you plan to raise it, the single most important part of any fund development effort is the strength of your relationships. Without powerful relationships, it's a constant uphill battle to develop a stronger board, impact major giving, expand grants, increase event income, or drive a successful capital campaign.

Let's Have Lunch Together tears down many of the relationship-building roadblocks that I've seen clients experience over the years. It paves the way, with a step-by-step system, to successful major giving and multi-million dollar campaigns—without taking big risks or spending a ton of money.

If you enjoy the thrill of uncovering treasure right in

your own backyard, you'll love what you'll learn inside this book. Follow Oscar as he employs his greatest fundraising tool—himself—and fulfills every Executive Director's dream.

He's never heavy-handed or manipulative. For the first time, people can't do enough for him and the organization.

Oscar's successes are not fiction. They're very real. Our clients actually made all of this happen, and much more. Oscar did it by learning how to build stronger relationships and making them work for everyone. Now you can make more of your own miracles happen, too.

Follow his journey as he transforms a $500 donor into a $10,000 annual giver, strangers into $25,000 major gift donors, and a friend who donates sodas for events into a supporter who helps him raise $250,000 each and every year. Those are only a few of the very real miracles Oscar performs.

Step-by-step, you'll see exactly how he converts his board into a powerful leadership team and turns an unhappy donor into his strongest community advocate—an advocate who subsequently helps him raise hundreds of thousands of dollars.

There's probably a little bit of Oscar in all of us. He's deeply committed, has a strong vision, and works extremely hard. Like most Executive Directors, he's challenged by time, staff, and a tightening budget. He fears things will stay the same *and* he fears things will change.

Suddenly, one day at noon, Victoria, his new board

chair, unexpectedly drops by his office. Oscar was having a bad week—an extremely bad week. She was the last person he wanted to lunch with.

So it all began over a casual luncheon at Oscar's favorite diner: he learned how to build stronger relationships and make them work so much better than they ever had before.

If you're a nonprofit president, executive director, responsible for development, or member of a board, sit back and enjoy this book. Experience what a whole new world fundraising is with stronger relationships. Highlight some new ideas and give a few of them a try.

Call or e-mail me. Let me know how it's working for you.

Marshall Howard

1

Troubles Ahead

Finally, after eight years as Executive Director, Oscar now felt he had a real chance to move his organization to the next level. Without showing any emotions, he patiently awaited an important decision from a very influential major donor prospect. He had just finished a $50,000 lead gift ask to one of the most successful business couples in town, Janice Worthington and her husband Ted. The future of his new family center was riding on that one word, "Yes." Without their financial commitment, it would be very difficult to raise the $500,000 needed. They were his last and only hope!

Oscar could feel the tension build. Silence filled the Worthington's small, oak-paneled conference room. He was confident that they would say yes. After all, he had made an excellent case for the family center.

The silence seemed to go on forever. There wasn't a single question from either one of them. It was nerve-wracking.

Perhaps this would be a good time to say a quick prayer, he thought to himself. The couple continued to examine the proposal, occasionally glancing up at Oscar.

How could they possibly turn down a golden opportunity like this? They could make a big impact. I've done everything by the book. We had a perfect introduction a few months ago through a long-time supporter. Our first meeting sparked their interest. They saw our mission in action, then asked me for specifics in writing. I wrote a very thorough proposal.

As the Worthingtons quietly discussed the project between themselves, Oscar began to feel increasingly optimistic. Had he noticed a couple of positive nods?

There they go again. Yup, that's definitely a nod, all right. There's another one.

He could hardly contain his excitement. He wanted to leap out of his chair and yell, "*Yes! We've finally done it!*"

Oscar couldn't take anymore of this drama. Thoughts raced through his mind about who would be the new program lead, where it would be housed, and how it would be introduced to the community.

Okay, folks, just say "yes" already!

He knew it would be impossible for Janice and Ted to turn down a project as important as this.

Oscar finally broke the silence. "What do you think?"

They slowly began to rise out of their chairs. Both had a smile on their face.

It was in the bag, he excitedly thought to himself.

"I can see you put a lot of work into this proposal, Oscar. The program is something that's definitely needed by many families in our city, but..."

Oh, no. This is definitely not the time for buts.

"...we'd like to think about it a little more," they continued.

He stood up and once again asked them, "Did the proposal give you a good overview? I hope it explains the urgent need for these services."

"You've done a great job," said Janice. "As I've said before, you've covered all the bases for us extremely well."

Oscar felt very proud.

"We just need a little more time to think about it."

There was a jolt of disappointment that shot through Oscar's body. "I understand," he said graciously, as they all walked toward the door. "Call me if there's anything else you need. I look forward to your support."

Although they didn't say yes, Oscar was still confident Janice and Ted would be the ones to take his organization to the next level. On his way out, he shook both their hands firmly as if to say, *I'm glad you are aboard.*

He pulled out of the parking lot, slipped his favorite CD into the player of his new Volvo, and gave out a long sigh of relief. *Asking for $50,000 is not something I'm accustomed to doing, nor is it one of the favorite parts of my job. I don't like to sell or be sold. But if I say so myself, I think it turned out darn good. All signs point to that wonderful three-letter word I like to hear: "Yes! Yes! Yes!"*

* * *

Plowing through morning traffic, he couldn't stop thinking about how the Worthingtons' contribution would be the one, bright, shining light in an otherwise lackluster fundraising year.

To continue that rare positive feeling, Oscar forced himself not to think about all of his organization's challenges: his ongoing, two-year struggle to build a more influential board; his perpetual battles to offset decreasing and more restrictive grants; and his never-ending uphill fight to increase annual campaign and special events revenue.

As Executive Director, he knew his fundraising world was changing, and changing very fast. *Perhaps with the help of folks like the Worthingtons*, he thought, *we'll now be able to establish an endowment and build our major gift and planned giving programs.* Oscar clearly understood that those were the yellow brick roads of fundraising—the hallmarks of a mature fund development program.

After running a few business errands, he returned to his office several hours later. He immediately noticed his message light was rapidly blinking at him. *Maybe it's the Worthingtons?*

Without hesitation, he began to retrieve his calls. A voice said, "You have five new messages."

He listened to message one. It wasn't them. Then he scrolled through messages two and three. Again, not a word from the Worthingtons. Message four was his wife. She was calling to see if this would be one of those rare nights he'd be home in time for dinner.

As he began to listen to the last message, a troubled look came over his face. It was Bob Dailey, one of Oscar's great board catches. He listened intently as he heard Bob say, "Oscar, I'd like to meet with you as soon as possible. Is the day after tomorrow, Thursday, at your office, convenient for you?"

That was enough to break Oscar's major gift celebration party. Bob's tone of voice could only mean one thing: trouble with a capital T.

Bob was an influential banker and a community leader—someone most executive directors dreamed about having on their board. His commitment was vital to the organization's future. Problems with Bob could spell disaster for Oscar's long-term plans.

He immediately returned Bob's call and confirmed Thursday's meeting for 9:00 a.m. When Oscar tried to ask Bob why he wanted to meet, he would only say, "I've had some things on my mind and I want to talk to you about them."

Oscar slumped back in his chair. Although he was sometimes frustrated with his board, he just couldn't figure out why, all of a sudden, Bob wanted to meet with him. *Have I gone too far*, he thought, *trying to get board members more engaged in our fundraising efforts?*

There wasn't much he could do now about Bob's meeting except wait and worry until Thursday.

* * *

His anxiety-filled week wasn't quite over yet. There was more trouble ahead. He spent the rest of his day working on issues for next year's budget. The new family center was a big piece of it.

As the end of the day approached, there was a light knock on his door. It was Madeline Aguilar, his Director of Development.

"Hi, Oscar. Do you have a minute? There's something I want to talk to you about."

"Absolutely. Have a seat. I've been meaning to call you," he said. "I want to tell you all about the great meeting this morning with the Worthingtons. They thought it was an excellent proposal."

For over two-and-a-half years, Oscar could always depend on Madeline. They seemed to have the same workstyle.

Although we haven't had the best of fundraising years,

thought Oscar, *nobody works or tries harder than she does. She understands teamwork and the importance of follow-through. She's a very valuable member of our staff.*

From the moment they sat down, however, Oscar sensed there was something different about her today. She seemed troubled.

After Oscar finished highlighting the meeting with Janice and Ted Worthington, Madeline immediately chimed in. "It sounds like it was very productive, Oscar. I'm curious, what other organizations are they involved with? Do they have any kids? How old are they? Are they originally from here?"

"I'm not sure those were appropriate questions to ask them," he responded. "But I do know they liked the proposal. I'm confident we'll get their $50,000 lead gift for the family center."

Madeline had an amazed look on her face. Instantly, Oscar had just confirmed why she needed to talk to him.

"What did you want to see me about?" Oscar asked tentatively.

Madeline began to shift in her chair and move some papers over to one side of the table. All of a sudden, he felt she was going to tell him something he did not want to hear. "This is not easy to discuss with you, Oscar..."

Instantly, that familiar knot in his stomach began to form. *Please don't say what I think you're going to say.*

"I believe 100% in our mission and the work we're

doing here, but I'm not sure Director of Development is the job for me. I'm not sure I'm cut out to be a fundraiser for a nonprofit. I've thought about going back to banking. I came in here to talk to you about resigning."

After what seemed to be hours of silence, Oscar leaned over, placed his elbows on the table, and said to Madeline in a calming tone, "Talk to me more about what's troubling you about your job."

"It's not that I don't think our work is important. It is. We're making a big difference," Madeline continued, "It's just that I feel very frustrated much of the time."

"How so?"

"I feel as if I'm continuously taking two steps forward and then three steps backwards. Each year, we run from event to event always struggling to find new supporters to make them a bit more profitable. There's got to be a better way to raise money."

Oscar was surprised Madeline was being so direct. He continued to listen.

"Oscar, I think things would improve if somehow we could get to know our donors better. I feel that most of them barely know us, nor we them. That makes it so much harder for us to increase our funding."

Oscar was upset. *We've always had good relationships with our supporters. Nothing has ever led me to believe otherwise,* he thought to himself. *Besides, our donor relationships are Madeline's responsibilities. She's the Director of Development.*

That's her job.

"Oscar, the Worthingtons are a good example of what I'm talking about. It seems to me we still don't know much about them, and they probably don't know enough about us. How can we realistically expect $50,000 from people with whom we don't have a very strong relationship? That's a lot of money from almost strangers."

Oscar felt as if he had just been kicked in the stomach. "Believe me, Madeline, as Executive Director, I understand the importance of having strong donor relationships," he said emphatically. "It's something I'm continuously trying to build and improve upon."

Although he respected and liked Madeline, his patience was wearing thin. "If you've felt that there was a problem with our donor relationships, why, over all these years, haven't you done something about it?"

"I've tried. Every time we talk about our fundraising, you and the development committee just come up with yet another event or new idea of the year. We've never once discussed ways to grow stronger relationships with our donors. In the long run, that's what will help us raise even more money."

"I fully agree. Why don't you build those relationships on your own, like I try to do?"

"Oscar, I wish I had more time and the flexibility to do exactly that. I'm so busy writing proposals, handling community relations, and managing all of our fundraisers, I barely have time for my own family. You've made it perfectly clear those are my priorities and responsibilities."

Although Oscar was irritated, he definitely wanted her to stay. "Madeline, look at all the great things you're doing here. Your work is helping so many families. Do you remember when Anita and her children came over to say thanks for the help?"

"How could I possibly forget? I had tears in my eyes."

"Those are the results we're accomplishing every day."

"But Oscar, don't you see, we could accomplish so much more if we somehow could focus on building stronger relationships. Each year, we keep looking for a panacea or a quick new fix. That's wearing me out."

He knew Madeline was right about relationships. It was *how* to build those relationships and *how* to turn them into great things that he could never quite figure out.

"I'm not trying to change your feelings about your work," Oscar continued, "nor am I trying to change your mind about leaving."

"I understand perfectly," said Madeline.

"Then do me a favor," he asked. "Do you think you could hold off on making a final decision for at least forty-five days?"

Before talking to Oscar, she already had made up her mind to leave. On the other hand, she also felt she owed him the extra time.

"Oscar, I told you the way I see it because I believe in the organization and our work. As Executive Director, I thought you needed to hear it. I'll stay for another forty-five days, but I don't think things will change."

Oscar stood up and walked her to the door. "Relationships are critical to our success. I appreciate you telling me how you feel. Thanks for giving it another month or so."

Oscar knew he had just dodged a bullet, barely. What he didn't know was exactly what more he could possibly do to build those stronger donor relationships.

"People say yes To those they know best."

2

Lightning Hits Twice

Emotionally drained from the day, Oscar put a stack of papers in his briefcase for night reading, turned off the lights, and headed for home.

After dinner, he reclined in his favorite easy chair, trying to forget work and relax for the evening. As hard as Oscar tried, his thoughts continually drifted back to the Worthington's major ask meeting, Bob Dailey's urgent appointment, and Madeline's resignation.

He put his head back and closed his eyes. *Was Madeline right about the Worthingtons? Did I make a major misstep with Bob? How can I keep a valuable employee from leaving?*

Instead of relaxing, Oscar grew more and more

agitated. Just then, his wife Debra came into the room. "It's nice to have you home at a reasonable hour for a change. But you seem upset, Oscar. What's the problem?"

"I wish it was only one problem," he replied. As he told her about the day's events, his anxiety slowly gave way, once again, to a deep, gut-wrenching feeling in the pit of his stomach. "I don't know if it's me, the economy we're in, or it's all because of a full moon, but things all of a sudden aren't going well."

"It's not you, Oscar. You put your heart and soul into your work, not to mention the hours and energy. No one is more dedicated. Just be positive."

"You're right, Debra. I'm doing everything I possibly can. Nobody can say the organization hasn't grown as rapidly as we hoped because of a lack of trying."

"Come on, Oscar, let's go upstairs. It's almost eleven o'clock."

* * *

Wednesday morning came all too fast for Oscar. He arrived at the office about twenty minutes before the rest of the staff, made some coffee, and tried to prepare for his weekly staff meeting.

He couldn't stop thinking about all the possible reasons why Bob might want to meet with him. *Did he know about Madeline's possible resignation? Was there a problem with* the Worthingtons? Was he coming over to give his usual words of wisdom about how to increase the annual campaign, grant funding, or special events income?

During most of the meeting, Oscar struggled to concentrate on the business at hand. *I wonder if any of the staff notice that I'm not my usual self today? This is not at all typical of me. On the other hand, this is not shaping up to be a typical week.*

Throughout the seemingly long morning, Oscar couldn't wait until noon. He was looking forward to getting out of the office. Wednesdays gave him a rare opportunity to chat it up with friends at his Rotary luncheon.

Although there were usually hundreds of Rotarians crowded into a 1960s-style room, Oscar's six to eight buddies always made the large group feel more comfortable to him. Occasionally, he would stray beyond his circle of friends to meet and say hello to other members.

After all that's happened over the past few days, he thought to himself as he listened to the speaker, *I'm enjoying the diversion of this week's Rotary luncheon all the more.*

Upon returning to the office, he flipped through his messages like a deck of cards. There it was, standing out like a beacon in the night: a phone call from the Worthingtons. "It's about time. They've finally decided!"

Quickly, pushing some papers aside, he grabbed the phone and immediately called them back.

"Hello," a voice answered. "Worthington and Company."

"This is Oscar Shelton, returning the Worthingtons' call." He could hardly contain his excitement. All his hard work was about to pay off.

"Let me see if they're available. They may be in a long meeting," a pleasant voice responded.

The receptionist's 30-second hold seemed like hours. "They're just finishing up. If you'd like to wait a few more minutes, they'll both be available, or they can call you back."

"It's okay, I'll wait for them." He wasn't about to prolong this moment of victory any longer.

As the minutes rolled by, the tension mounted. Sweat formed like pools in Oscar's palms. He could barely keep the phone from slipping out of his hand.

All of a sudden, the receptionist came on the line. "Sorry for the delay, Mr. Shelton, they'll be with you in a moment. Thanks for your patience."

By this point, patience was something he was slowly running out of. "Where are they?" he kept repeating to himself. "Where are they?"

Just then, Ted came on the line. Oscar was somewhat startled. "Hello Oscar, I'm so glad you called us right back. We wanted to talk to you as soon as possible."

Janice then joined them. "Hi Oscar, hope your day is going well."

"Excellent. Thank you."

By the upbeat tone of their voices, Oscar was more certain then ever they were going to be his $50,000 lead sponsor.

This time, Ted did most of the talking. "Oscar, there's little doubt the new family project is something that's terribly needed by families throughout the city. Janice and I feel honored you came to us with this opportunity."

Suddenly, Oscar was beginning to feel an emotional jolt. He just wasn't sure if it was up or down.

"We've given this a great deal of thought," Ted continued. "We know it's an important decision for many people."

As usual, Oscar just wanted to get to the bottom line. *You know you're going to say yes, probably with some strings attached, so please come out with it already.*

"Ted's right," said Janice. "Your project is an important long term commitment."

"That's true," responded Oscar. "It has to work for everyone."

"Although we fully agree that the center is needed," said Ted, "we unfortunately have to decline at this time."

No! That's impossible. Everything was going so well. Oscar felt totally devastated. He couldn't say anything. *This is now the end of the Worthingtons. This is the end of my project that I've worked so hard to launch.*

"Oscar, we hope you'll see this as the beginning of a long partnership," continued Ted. "As we get to know you, your organization, and understand better the work you do. I'm sure there will be many opportunities to help."

"$50,000 is a substantial commitment," added Janice. "Over the past couple of months, we've been very impressed with what we've seen. However, the organizations that Ted and I have strong relationships with over many years also need our help. Those are the groups we want and need to financially support. I hope you'll understand."

Oscar was speechless and very disappointed. He could only say, "I do," although he really did not. "In the future, I look forward to both of you becoming active in our organization." He didn't go any further.

"Thank you, Oscar," they said together.

Oscar's hand was shaking as he hung up the phone. He sat at his desk motionless. He thought to himself, *Perhaps Madeline was right in her assessment about the Worthingtons. What more could I have possibly done?*

It was late afternoon. Oscar had about all he could take for one day. He decided to pack up some work to do at home, then head out that evening to his final softball game of the fall league.

Spending a couple of hours under the shimmering lights on a baseball diamond with friends was, tonight of all nights, a welcome oasis. The only thing Oscar and his teammates had the luxury of thinking about was winning. He would worry about all those other things tomorrow.

"Money goes Where the relationship flows."

3

Last Strike

Although Thursday morning was brisk and sunny, it seemed a little gray to Oscar. He was still thinking about Janice and Ted. *It's going to be a very long time before I find another possible donor like the Worthingtons. I had such high expectations. What went wrong?* he thought as he sat at his desk and poured his first cup of coffee.

As 9:00 a.m. slowly approached, he tried to mentally prepare himself for his meeting with Bob. As much as he thought about it, he still had no idea why, all of a sudden, Bob wanted to meet with him.

Oscar didn't like surprises—especially from board members. Tension seemed to slowly fill his office. He jolted up from behind his desk and began to nervously pace, waiting for Bob's arrival.

All of a sudden, the buzz of his intercom jolted him. "It's Bob Dailey for you, Oscar. He's here for your meeting."

Oscar walked out into the lobby to greet him. "Good morning, Bob," he said cheerfully. "I'm glad we could meet. I've been looking forward to it."

The two of them went into Oscar's office. As Bob followed, he noticed him gently closing the door. Oscar slowly raised his eyebrows. *That is definitely not a good sign.*

They exchanged pleasantries for a few minutes. Oscar wanted him to get right down to business. "Tell me, Bob, what exactly did you have on your mind?"

Bob leaned forward in his chair. "As you know, Oscar, I've been on the board for a little over a year. I've appreciated the opportunity you've given me to serve and make a difference…"

Oh, no, Oscar thought to himself, *I don't like the way this is beginning. It feels like the overture to both Madeline's and the Worthington's meeting.*

"…let me tell you why I wanted to meet."

"Please do," said Oscar anxiously.

"I'm going to resign from the board. Let me explain…"

Oscar was shocked. He felt totally devastated. His most prominent and influential supporter was abandoning ship. He didn't know what to say, but he definitely wanted to know why. "I don't understand."

"There are several reasons, Oscar. I've sat on many nonprofit boards in this city. It takes a great deal of my time and it's a lot of work. Especially in times like these."

"If anybody knows that, I do," said Oscar.

"To make that kind of commitment," Bob continued, "I need to feel I'm making a difference. When I feel connected and when there are mutual goals, I have the energy and motivation to go the extra mile to make that difference."

"Are you saying that you don't feel connected and that you don't feel you've made a difference over the past year?"

"Unfortunately, that's exactly what I am saying," replied Bob. "I really wanted our association to work. I don't feel it has. We've never discussed my role as a board member. Oscar, you and I have never once talked about why I joined the board, nor discussed any of my expectations. I don't ever recall us exploring ways in which you and I could work together to make that difference."

Oscar was stunned. "I never thought about that. I assumed you saw our mission as a worthy cause."

"I do, but it's more than that, Oscar. There are thousands of worthy causes and millions of nonprofits teeming with people who have good intentions. I had a special reason for joining. Do you know why?"

"What was it?" inquired Oscar curiously.

"It just so happens I came from a family similar to those we serve!"

Embarrassment could hardly describe the way Oscar was feeling. He knew Bob was right. He should have assumed less and asked more questions. But he didn't want to pry into Bob's personal life.

"I'm sorry to be so direct. I think it's important for you and the future of this organization to hear some of the reasons why I'm resigning."

Oscar had a puzzled look on his face, as if to say, *I always thought I knew Bob well—that I was open and understood people. That's why I'm doing this kind of work.*

Immediately, Bob seemed to read him.

"Perhaps I can put it another way: relationships!"

Oscar could not believe what he was hearing. *Relationships—that's the exact same word Madeline used in her resignation meeting a few days before. The Worthingtons also talked about strong relationships when they turned down the lead gift opportunity for the family center.*

Bob continued to explain. "For example, I think it's paramount for board members to get to know the staff and they us. I also wish there were more opportunities to learn about the families we serve and exactly how we serve them. I've only met one family briefly. Those things are all important to me.

It was very difficult for Oscar to hear this, especially from Bob, whom he highly respected. *Why didn't Bob talk to me about all of this before now?*

"Remember about a year ago, I introduced my

friends, the Jasons, to the organization? They became a $2,500 dinner sponsor."

"Absolutely," said Oscar. "That was great of you."

"Unfortunately, over the past year, they've become a little put off."

"How so?" Oscar nervously inquired.

"They've been contacted three times since. Each and every time there was a contact, they were continually asked for money for one project or another. There wasn't even a pretense about trying to educate them about our work, nor any effort made to build a relationship with them. It became apparent to them, and to me, that they had money and you wanted it. That was personally embarrassing."

Oscar sat like a deer caught in the headlights—a position he was unaccustomed to being in.

"In my experience, Oscar, if you want to grow and move the organization to the next level, understanding the importance of strong relationships and knowing how to build and keep them is not an option—it's absolutely essential. Perhaps it's something you should think about."

Oscar didn't appreciate what seemed to be a lecture. He knew there was little he could say or do to change Bob's mind. "Thanks for your candor. Do you think you might reconsider and stay?"

"Things would really need to change. I don't see that happening. I wish you the best in the future," said Bob as he stood up, shook Oscar's hand, and walked towards the door.

"I hope you'll take my comments in the spirit in which they were intended. I hope you'll find them helpful."

"Absolutely. You've given me much to think about."

* * *

Once Bob left, Oscar's feeling gradually moved from surprise to one of resentment. *Someone would have to live alone in a cave not to understand the importance of relationships or how to build them,* he thought. *It's insulting for him to tell me it's something I should think more about.*

However, as the day progressed, Oscar began to replay over and over again in his mind those three painful scenes with Madeline, the Worthingtons, and Bob. He began to see one common thread.

Madeline's lack of strong relationships with donors was, for her, like a tight bridle on a horse, he thought as he stared out his office window. *It held her back from raising money, helping more families, and made her job less satisfying and less enjoyable. She's about to leave me.*

The Worthingtons had no long-term, compelling relationship with me nor with the organization. That made all the difference. Their resources went to nonprofits with whom they had strong ties. I don't know enough people like the Worthingtons—and the few who I do know, I don't know well enough. Now my project is dead in the water.

Bob's lack of a strong relationship with the organization

was, for him, like a giant concrete dam. It prevented his powerful resources from flowing. I lost one of my most valuable board members and someone I admired greatly.

Ever so slowly, the pieces of a very important puzzle were finally coming together. Oscar was beginning to understand the high price he was now paying for not having those strong relationships. For the first time, he thought about how much his lack of solid relationships might have cost him in his board development and fundraising efforts. Was this just the tip of the iceberg?

What am I not doing? he kept asking himself. *What more can I do?*

That evening, on his big wooden deck at home, he lay back and enjoyed a rare Indian summer's night. Alone in his thoughts, he looked up to see the stars lighting the heavens into eternity. Everything seemed calm.

All of a sudden out of nowhere, an avalanche of panic cascaded through him. It engulfed his whole body. Fear seemed to take over. A cold sweat descended over him. He had never experienced something like this before. For the first time, he felt things were beginning to fall apart.

I've been Executive Director for over eight years. I thought I was smart enough to know all about the importance of relationships and how to build and keep them. Obviously, I'm not doing such a good job of it, he said angrily to himself. *The problems we're having are probably all my fault. There's no one else to blame.*

He jumped out of the lounge chair and began pacing around the patio. *If I don't do something and do it now, the organization and the families that we help could all suffer. I could lose my job.*

Oscar quickly ran into the house and splashed cold water on his face. This seemed to revive him. *"What's wrong?"* he said calmly. *"I need some answers, and I need them now!"*

It wasn't that Oscar didn't understand the importance of relationships. He absolutely did. Like so many others, however, he just couldn't solve one of life's biggest puzzles: how to build strong relationships with those who are important to him.

People always liked Oscar. He was friendly, cordial to everyone, and had a strong vision for his organization. Supporters never had an unkind word to say. Although somewhat shy, he had lots of friends who would do anything for him. He liked the staff and his staff liked him. At every turn, Oscar would always thank his donors. He would recognize their efforts in newsletters and in the annual report. Publicly, he always went out of his way to recognize their achievements. Oscar just couldn't figure out what more he could do, or what he could do differently.

"Knowing the whys
Eliminates the surprise."

Unexpected Visitor

As dawn broke on a cloudy Friday morning, Oscar, as usual, arrived at his office early. He didn't let on to anyone what was troubling him.

He decided to spend most of the morning visiting staff in their offices, just to see how things were going. He wasn't ready yet to tell Madeline about Bob or the Worthingtons. That could wait.

The morning flew by. It was noon. In typical Oscar fashion, he had a very set routine for lunchtime. Once a week, he'd join other staff in the resource room, twice a week he ate in his office, Wednesdays were, of course, Rotary. On Thursdays, he liked to frequent his favorite diner.

As he was about to go down the hall to get his lunch

out of the refrigerator, he heard a familiar voice at his door.

"Hello Oscar, I hope you don't mind me dropping in like this."

"Not at all," Oscar replied. "It's always a pleasure to see you."

It was Victoria Webster, his new board chair.

"What brings you over to this side of town?" he asked.

"I had some things to take care of a few blocks away at the Oxford Hotel. It's almost 12:30. Let's have lunch together."

"Lunch? Lunch?" he stammered.

"What say you and I grab a sandwich together at that favorite diner of yours?"

Oscar was totally surprised. *Why is Victoria suddenly asking me out to lunch? What's the problem now? She must know about Bob, even Madeline, and probably the Worthington's decision, too.*

"Sure, that sounds like a good idea. I was just on my way out for lunch anyway."

After arriving at the diner, they quickly ordered. Oscar tried to start a conversation.

"Is the Oxford Hotel one of your clients?" He knew Victoria was in commercial real estate.

"Oh no. I was making arrangements for a reunion party," she replied.

Oscar was somewhat curious, but he felt he didn't

know Victoria quite well enough to go any further. Besides, in typical Oscar fashion, he wanted to get down to business. *After all*, he thought, *I'm extremely lucky to have Victoria as my chair. She's very well-known and highly respected. Most executive directors would give anything to have a 20-year veteran volunteer and a former United Way campaign co-chair like Victoria aboard. I don't want to waste any of her valuable time.*

Then he let Victoria take the lead. They talked about the economy, skiing, and one of Victoria's favorite subjects, wine and foods. This light conversation puzzled him.

She must know about Bob and the Worthingtons. She's just waiting for the right moment to spring it on me.

They were halfway through lunch when, for some unknown reason, Oscar's curiosity got the better of him. "Are you having a school or family reunion at the Oxford?"

"Not quite," answered Victoria. "We're having a reunion for all the players on my golf team at State University."

Oscar was shocked. "You were on one of their famous golf teams?"

"Not exactly," she responded. "I was on the golf team all right, but long before it rose to national prominence. I was good, but not that good."

Oscar was baffled. Why hadn't anyone mentioned this to him before?

"Then I went to Stanford for my MBA and eventually got my law degree," Victoria continued. "When State

University's Coach Warren retired, they asked me to head up the program. I stayed for about two years."

Oscar was speechless. He didn't know Victoria was a lawyer, had an MBA, or even coached golf.

"Should I call you *coach* from now on?"

"Not right now," Victoria laughed.

That was the ice-breaker. The conversation between them took off. The questions flowed. Oscar found out about how Victoria made the transition from coach to CEO of the city's largest commercial real estate company, about her other nonprofit work, her family, her hobbies, and her vision for Oscar's organization.

The two of them talked endlessly for almost half an hour. They shared stories, thoughts, and goals.

Oscar was not only pleasantly surprised he could talk so long with Victoria, he was more surprised he could talk so long with her on subjects other than those about the organization.

For the first time, he felt more comfortable with Victoria. One might even say he felt more connected to her as a person, and not just connected to her as his board chair.

* * *

Oscar was about to take a bold step. He was about to do something he was very unaccustomed to doing: asking a board member for advice. "Victoria, some critical events have happened over this past week that could seriously affect our organization."

Oscar briefly told her about Madeline's possible leaving, the Worthingtons' turndown, and Bob's board resignation. He even explained the major reason they had given him which shaped their decisions: relationships.

"Frankly, Victoria, at this point, I'm not sure what to do. What's your read on this? You have a lot of experience in matters like these."

Victoria smiled, took a sip of coffee, and slowly leaned forward in her chair.

"Over the last couple of years as a board member, I've always appreciated any opportunity to help you, Oscar. First, let me say I know all about the Worthingtons. I heard this morning. News around here travels fast. I also know all about Bob's decision to resign. He called me a few days ago and we had a short conversation. I told him he needed to talk to you directly."

"I had no idea that he wanted to resign until we met," responded Oscar.

"Frankly, I wasn't all that surprised," she said. "I've known Bob for many years. We've worked on several boards together. We can discuss both of them a little later. There's something else I think we should talk about."

Oscar had a puzzled look on his face. *What could possibly be more important than Bob and the Worthingtons?*

"Something else?" Oscar asked hesitantly.

"I'm glad to hear you're open to some new ideas. Since you asked for my input, it seems as if you may be ready to think about some changes!"

"I can honestly say change is not one of my favorite things," replied Oscar laughingly.

"That's probably true for most people. But after this week's events, I think perhaps you should take a closer look at our organization's relationship strategy."

"What relationship strategy?" questioned Oscar.

"That's my point. Everyone knows relationships are very important. But not everyone knows how to build more powerful relationships. It's done through a well-executed relationship strategy."

"We're very well-respected and have a solid reputation in the community," he responded quickly.

"It's so much more than that, Oscar. Every successful organization, whether it has five employees or five hundred, has a well-developed relationship strategy. Today, it's not good enough to have great products or services, or, in our case as a nonprofit, just to be excellent stewards of our donor's money and produce great results."

"I know. That's why I always make an extra effort to recognize and thank our supporters and staff," he said somewhat defensively.

"You're absolutely right, you do. But that's only a very small part of a relationship strategy."

Oscar was beginning to take Victoria's comments

personally.

"Our organization has very dedicated staff and well meaning supporters," she said in a positive tone. "Our programs are efficient and produce top results. We've got the basics down pretty well."

Oscar was perplexed. *The basics?* he thought. *Running a nonprofit is not like coaching golf or selling and managing real estate. Nonprofits are very different.*

"Bob's reasons for resigning, the Worthingtons' reasons for declining, and even Madeline's frustrations, probably highlight a serious gap we may have in our relationship strategy model," reflected Victoria. "It could be we're not implementing the three critical parts of the model as well as we could."

By now, Oscar was becoming visibly irritated. *Gap? Model? We're not selling copiers, we're helping families. Perhaps asking for Victoria's advice may not have been such a good idea after all.*

"Relax, Oscar, this is not about you. First, it's about how successfully organizations engage the right people who are important to them; second, build strong partnerships with those people; and third, turn those relationships into productive results. There are even some organizations that don't yet fully understand the critical role relationships actually play in helping them reach their goals. They're so transactional, they're not even in the game yet."

"That's definitely not us," Oscar quickly responded.

"But tell me a little more about those three key parts to a relationship strategy."

"Both as a longtime volunteer and businesswoman, I've always looked upon relationships as the single most valuable resource, or asset, a person and an organization can have. Relationship assets are just like financial, program, or human resource ones. Your relationship assets need to be actively developed and grown. Without strong relationship assets, organizations miss opportunities, work harder, and struggle to reach goals. They become transactional…"

"Transactional? We've always prided ourselves on being high-touch," Oscar immediately interjected. "Where's the gap?"

Victoria knew from experience that often the organization was indeed too transactional. She didn't challenge him, she just continued.

"When not enough strong, mutually beneficial, win-win relationships with the right stakeholders have been crafted, organizations have a relationship asset gap. And that gap slows them down and consistently costs them dearly!"

There was a long pause. Oscar was in deep thought. He reflected on Bob, Madeline, the Worthingtons, and the very high price that he and the families they served were now paying.

"Are you beginning to see what's happening?"

"I think so," responded Oscar. "You're saying strong relationships with the right people are extremely important assets of the organization. They help me reach my goals. Without them, I have a costly gap. I have to work even harder because I'm not operating with all of the resources I could have."

"Exactly. It's like driving your car without all of the cylinders—not too efficient."

"Victoria, I know we have to find and engage the right people. That's always been a big challenge."

"That's the first important step in implementing a successful relationship strategy: capturing the right stakeholders. It's also important to continually grow and manage each key stakeholder. That's called developing win-win relationships—the second step of a relationship strategy. Good relationship managers deliver lots of wins to their stakeholders by really getting to know them as a person. In turn, the stakeholder also gets to know you, so they want to deliver more of your wins."

Victoria was beginning to cross a line that was making him feel uncomfortable. Oscar continued to listen. He said nothing.

"Finally, it's knowing how and when to turn those relationships into great outcomes — identifying all the different resources a stakeholder has. That's the third step of a good relationship strategy. Just having strong relationships with the right people isn't enough. It's also the ability to make great things happen with those relationships. Remember, clay is only mud until it gets into the artist's hands."

Oscar couldn't hold back any longer. "Wait a minute," he suddenly interjected again. "Are you talking about manipulating people and taking advantage of your relationships with them?"

"Not at all. It's just the opposite. Have you ever experienced that when you have a good, solid relationship with someone, they'll help you when asked? In business, that's called a partnership. In our personal life, that's called friendship."

"That's true," said Oscar. "Some of my oldest and closest friends have always come through for me, in big ways every time."

Although he appreciated Victoria's input, Oscar was still very skeptical that she could show him anything new about how to find new supporters or how to build stronger relationships. "So the way you see it," he said to Victoria, "there are three major steps to a successful relationship strategy."

"That's correct."

Oscar always carried a small notebook. He read from the notes he had just written. "One, capture the right stakeholders. Two, develop strong win-win relationships. Three, turn relationships into productive outcomes."

"You've got them down exactly. Oscar, there are so many exciting upsides for a nonprofit that has a strong relationship strategy working for them."

"Such as?" Now he was curious to hear more.

"Above all, a strong relationship strategy is the most cost-effective way to fundraise. You don't have to spend a ton of money. Net returns are extremely high, it's very predictable, benefits are long-term, and it's not risky. That's not to say events aren't still important—they are. Within a finely tuned relationship strategy, I've seen organizations triple or quadruple their event income in one year and reach hundreds of new stakeholders."

Cheaper, less risk, more money, long-term, thought Oscar. *It sounds too good to be true.*

"Since you seem to be interested, walk me back to the Oxford where I left my car. We can continue our conversation."

Oscar's Notebook

"Relationship tactics make best practices."

◆ Relationships = key assets of the organization

◆ Weaker relationships = working harder, missing opportunities, slower growth, donor turnover.

◆ Stronger relationships = lower costs, higher returns, minimum risk, long-term benefits.

◆ Three steps that build a powerful relationship strategy are:
     1. Capture the right stakeholders
     2. Develop win-win relationships
     3. Turn relationships into productive outcomes

5

The Big Catch

The more Oscar thought about the three steps and all the upsides to a relationship strategy, a million thoughts raced through his mind. Outside the hotel parking lot, he finally turned to Victoria and said, "There are also many other ways to increase our fundraising."

"That's true, Oscar, there are. But one of the most important ways to produce the biggest payoff, is a strong relationship."

"What's so special about those three major steps? We're already doing them the best we can."

"Oscar, you are. There just might be ways to do some things differently to get even better results." Victoria pointed towards the lobby entrance. "Let's go inside and talk about it for a moment."

Somewhat reluctantly, Oscar walked into the hotel lobby. They sat down around a small glass table.

"How would you like to uncover some relationship-building secrets that people spend a lifetime trying to uncover?"

Suddenly, Victoria had piqued his interest.

"Oscar, there are a lot to those three steps."

"There are?"

"I think most people today would like to become better at building stronger relationships with those who are important to them."

"That's probably true. It's only recently that I've had to admit that."

"Well, you're in luck. Over the years, through my volunteer work and professional life, I've learned some ways that can make a huge difference. Ways that can help you engage some of the most influential, affluent leaders in town. Ways to build powerful partnerships that lead to incredible results. But there's a big catch."

"I knew there had to be. What is it?" he asked.

"I can coach you for years and you can spend a lifetime reading about ways to build productive relationships. But if you want any of this to work, you'll need to make three commitments to yourself. Promises you may not like right now."

"Such as?" Oscar asked hesitantly.

"First, a commitment to make a few changes. Second, a commitment to give up some of your old comfort zones and develop new ones using more of your strengths. Third, to take responsibility for developing stronger donor relationships—to make relationship-building an important part of your work."

Oscar was stunned. All he really wanted from Victoria were a few quick and easy tips on how to make his world work better. He didn't want her to totally remodel it.

"Those are some difficult promises," he said to her with a big lump in his throat.

"That's true, they are. If you don't make those commitments, nothing I say or do will make a difference. We don't have to go any further. I will certainly understand."

Oscar didn't know what to say. Victoria was not only his board chair, she was also his boss.

"If we go forward," added Victoria, "the centerpiece of our work will be a new leadership team I call a Partnership Council. It's a group of approximately twenty influential supporters. Virtually all of the members will be new to the organization. It won't be as hard to build as you think. I want you to know upfront, it will take time—about six to nine months to complete the first phase."

More and more, Oscar was feeling trapped. He had to say or do something, and he had to do it now.

"Victoria, I know today more than ever, strong relationships are important, especially for an organization like ours. I'm not sure this is the right time to start."

"What are you saying, Oscar?"

"I'm just so busy managing staff and programs, handling mountains of government requirements, and trying to raise money. Finding time and getting board involvement may be a problem right now."

His immediate response came as no surprise. There never is a right time to start something new. Although Victoria knew Oscar was smart, had lots of untapped strengths, and was deeply committed to his work, she also understood that change for most people is often uncomfortable. She wasn't about to let a good executive director—who could become great—off the hook that easily.

"Oscar, through my experiences coaching, managing, and volunteering for over twenty-five years, I've discovered that one of the most powerful forces that frequently controls us is fear. It's not usually our abilities that handcuff us, it's fear that holds us back."

"Fear? Fear of what?" said Oscar defensively. He wasn't about to let Victoria know what was troubling him.

"We fear things will stay the same. We fear things will change. Sometimes, thinking about the big, exciting payoffs helps to release us so we can go forward. Imagine, within two years, you could double the number of families we serve."

For the first time, a smile finally appeared on Oscar's face. He thought about all the great things he had always wanted to accomplish. If only he could unshackle himself.

"There's one more important thing. We're going to have to partner together as colleagues," said Victoria, "That means being more open and candid with each other."

"More as my coach?" Oscar said laughingly.

"Exactly. I think you should take some time, Oscar, and think about all of this. I'm perfectly all right with that. We can talk again in a couple of weeks."

"I appreciate that," he replied. He hoped that Victoria didn't think he was trying to sidestep his job.

As they left the hotel lobby and shook hands, Victoria turned to Oscar. "Your personal commitments are key. They can be far more important to your success than any of my coaching tips. Just let me know when you're ready."

It was late Friday afternoon. Oscar briefly went back to the office, packed up some weekend to-dos and headed for home.

* * *

An otherwise great two days at his family's cabin on the lake, fishing, relaxing and enjoying his friend's company turned into a struggle. No matter how hard he tried, Oscar's fears about the organization and his job continuously percolated in his mind.

Am I resisting Victoria's help because of a lack of time? he thought to himself. *We all have the same amount of time, yet why can some people use their time to get exactly what they want?*

Besides, what more could Victoria possibly teach me about relationships?

For almost a week, Oscar felt as if he was competing in a world championship wrestling match fighting against himself. He kept thinking about the theme of a book he had read on his last vacation, *Who Moved My Cheese?* He thought about his eight long years of hard work as executive director—how he was only inching closer to his goals. There was still such a long way to go.

Finally, late one evening, he had a breakthrough. He turned to his wife and said, "If I continue to do what I've always done, I'll continue to get what I've always gotten."

Oscar was at the point in his life where he didn't want to get any more of the same. He was now ready to make that important call.

"It's Oscar, how are you?"

"Excellent," responded Victoria. "I wasn't expecting to hear from you so soon."

"I think I'm ready to learn more about building relationships."

"I'm very pleased to hear that, Oscar. We'll probably have to meet about three times and teleconference to fill in the rest. How about starting off at 1:00 p.m. Friday at my office?"

"That works for me," he replied.

"Friday it is. You might want to bring your laptop."

Oscar's Notebook

*"Getting ready to start
Takes a change of heart."*

◆ It's not abilities that handcuff us, it's often fear—
fear things will stay the same, fear things will change.

◆ Envisioning how things could be unbinds the
shackles.

◆ Three personal promises that launch more powerful
relationships are:
   1. Commit to some changes now
   2. Develop new comfort zones using more of
      my strengths
   3. Become responsible for the organization's
      relationship assets

Unchartered Waters

Although Oscar was looking forward to his first coaching session with Victoria, he felt a little uneasy. He had never partnered with a board member this way before. He was both excited and nervous.

After entering her well-decorated 12th floor office, the receptionist escorted him into a large executive conference room.

"Would you like a cup of coffee or a cold drink, Mr. Shelton? Victoria is finishing up a call. She'll be with you in a few minutes."

"I'm all right," replied Oscar as he set up his computer for their first meeting.

He immediately noticed all the community service

awards proudly displayed on the walls. There must have been thirty of them, except one from his organization. He also noticed pictures of all her employees. Curiously, each employee was surrounded by his or her family, portrait style.

"Hello, Oscar," said Victoria as she came into the room. "Are you ready to get started?"

"I think so," he said a little nervously.

Victoria neatly spread her notes across the table. "Let's start off by talking about the first of our three relationship strategy steps: capturing the right stakeholders for our Partnership Council."

No sooner had she begun, than Oscar was already thinking about some shortcuts. "Last time we met, you mentioned a Council. I've given it some thought. Why not use our board of directors instead of going to all the trouble to build a new leadership team? That's what boards are for. That would save us a lot of time and effort."

Victoria could already see what was happening. "Frankly, Oscar, our board is composed of well-meaning people with good intentions. Some would make good Partnership Council members; others would not. I don't think most can help you do what you have to get done."

Oscar was shocked that Victoria was being so forthright. He just couldn't stop himself from asking, "Our current leadership isn't good enough?"

"Truthfully," Victoria paused for a moment, "just adequate. Good enough to get where we are today. Not good enough to get where we want to go."

"I've worked hard over many years trying to strengthen our board," said Oscar, somewhat defensively. "I know it's still not where it should be. It's going to take more time."

"You have worked very hard," said Victoria. "That's not the issue. You have a big challenge here. The types of powerful leaders needed always want to join groups with their peers. They want to link with people like themselves who have the potential to make big things happen, not waste their valuable time. So one of the first questions an influential prospective stakeholder will ask is, 'Who's involved?' If they don't see lots of their social and business peers engaged, that's already two major strikes."

Oscar thought about his board. There were several retirees, a teacher, a nurse, a couple of salespeople, three middle managers, and a few lawyers and accountants. Although it was the strongest board he had in years, except for Victoria, Bob Dailey, and maybe a couple of others, it wasn't an influential, affluent group.

"So how do I capture the right people? It's like the chicken and the egg principle."

"Here's another good principle to think about," Victoria added. "Why do people keep doing the same things over and over again expecting different results? You've spent a lot of time and energy trying to strengthen the board and raise more money. You should realize by now that's almost impossible to do the way you're going about it."

"Then how?" asked Oscar, frustrated.

"Are you ready to accept responsibility and some change? If so, I know you can raise that $500,000, and so much more."

"I guess I'm as ready as ever."

"Are you also ready not to waste time with shortcuts?"

"No shortcuts," Oscar promised.

"If you know a better and faster way to reach your goals and raise more money, by all means, share them with me," challenged Victoria. "I know for a fact this way works. I've experienced it firsthand."

"I don't," said Oscar. "If I did, I guess I'd already be doing it."

"Then let's continue to talk about how to capture the right people for our Partnership Council. You'll need to recruit about twenty new, influential, successful business and community leaders who are interested in our mission. The Council is our leadership and relationship-building incubator."

Oscar could already see this was far more work than he imagined. As Executive Director, he was already juggling so many balls. Besides, he wasn't so sure he wanted to develop a new team of volunteers.

"What exactly do you mean by a relationship incubator?" he asked curiously.

"Like most nonprofits, we presently have only two points of entry for great prospective stakeholders or existing donors to get more involved with us: our board or event committees. That's a problem. Most new people are certainly not ready to make a board commitment. Also, most influential leaders don't want to take their time and talents to simply join a committee to help organize another fundraising event. They want big results. So how do we get them involved?"

"Through a Partnership Council?" answered Oscar. It was starting to make more sense.

"Exactly. Do you have any questions so far? Now's the time to ask them."

There was absolute silence in the room. Oscar said nothing.

"I know we're a very grassroots, volunteer-driven organization," said Victoria as she broke the silence.

"That's very important," interjected Oscar. "I don't want to lose that."

"It is important. We won't lose our great base of supporters. To get to where you want to be, you'll not only need to build relationships with many new, influential stakeholders, but you'll also need to build much stronger relationships with our existing supporters."

"Are you saying there's room for all types of people in our relationship strategy?"

"Absolutely. There has to be, to make it work," said

Victoria emphatically. "Everyone counts in a well-designed relationship strategy."

"Tell me more." Oscar was beginning to feel a little more comfortable.

"The Partnership Council is truly a creature of beauty," joked Victoria. "Imagine one Council supporting many of our fundraising efforts. We'll recruit new supporters on the basis of our mission. Those people who say yes will join us because they have an interest in our work, not just because they like organizing events."

Victoria then continued to share her Council experiences—how she and each member chose to work on certain campaigns or events. Then they would build strong fundraising committees with their friends and colleagues outside the Council. Certain standout committee members were later asked to join the Partnership Council. Select Council members were ultimately asked to join the board.

"So you see, Oscar, the Partnership Council is our ongoing leadership and relationship-building incubator for business and community leaders of influence and affluence. It's a place to grow and develop our new leadership."

Oscar was confused. "What's the difference between the Partnership Council, our board, and the Development Committee?"

"There's a big difference. A Partnership Council gives us a strong point of entry to immediately and more easily recruit those 20 new, influential leaders we need. They'll join three to six of our stronger board members who we'll also recruit to be part of our Council. There are no fiduciary or management responsibilities. For most members, it's their first step with us. Most importantly, they're all peers focused on major projects producing big results. The Partnership Council is not a do-nothing advisory committee."

"I have one big concern, Victoria. It's been almost impossible for me to find even a handful of prominent new board members. How do you expect me to build an entire twenty member Partnership Council?"

"Because I expect you to learn the two fundamentals of capturing the right stakeholders and execute them extremely well—the same way lots of other organizations have built their powerful leadership teams."

"Fundamentals?" he asked. "What fundamentals?"

"Our first step, capture the right stakeholders, has two very important fundamentals: identify and recruit. I think it's time you learned more about them."

Oscar started thinking about some of the prominent groups in his town: Boy Scouts, YMCA, Children's Hospital, the Museum, and, most recently, the Boys and Girls Club.

How could Victoria expect me to convince those types of leaders to join us? he thought to himself. *Why would they even be interested? They're already committed and very busy. Besides, we're not high-profile enough for them.*

Oscar was still very skeptical.

"Remember, Oscar, those other groups, big and small,

didn't start out with a powerful leadership team. Whether it's mastering golf or increasing fundraising, it comes down to one thing and one thing only: how well you execute the fundamentals. That's the difference between an average golfer and a pro, or between receiving $250 from a donor versus $25,000."

Oscar thought about how he had typically tried to secure new board members and donors for the family project. He'd simply uncover a few good names, arrange a meeting, and make an ask. But the problem was he never had enough good prospective stakeholders nor had enough successful asks. Although this was all new to him, he realized things had to change, or he'd continually get more of the same.

"I'm about to share five steps to help you identify the right people. If you want to uncover hundreds of great potential stakeholders for the Partnership Council, you'll learn how to execute them very, very well."

Oscar entered the following steps into his laptop:

To Identify the Right People

1. Build a profile of the perfect stakeholder/Partnership Council member.
2. Search for and uncover prospective stakeholders from referrals and contributors.
3. Organize prospective stakeholders into a spreadsheet.
4. Evaluate each stakeholder's potential.
5. Prioritize who's to be contacted, how, and when.

"Oscar, to master the fundamentals of identifying the right stakeholders, it's important not to fall into two traps: money and power."

"I don't understand. Those are two of my favorite things."

"Don't chase money. Identify and chase strong leadership. Then the money will always come. That's the money trap."

Once again, Oscar thought about his visits with the Worthingtons. He had only talked to them about their financial contribution and what it would accomplish. He never once discussed with them their ongoing involvement— how their leadership would make an even bigger impact. He chased the money, not their leadership. He lost.

"Financial potential to give," continued Victoria, "may not necessarily be the most important criteria. It's only one of several."

"Why go after someone who doesn't have money?" inquired Oscar.

"They may hold another asset more valuable than money: the power to introduce you to many of their friends and colleagues who can also help. That's the power trap."

"So are you saying people like my pastor and my friend Walter, who's Assistant Superintendent of Schools, along with others who know the right people, are very important to our strategy?"

"Exactly. They're an excellent source of good referrals

and quality introductions. On the other hand, you may also want to consider some of those relationship holders for the Council. The Worthingtons and Bob are important, not simply because of their own financial capacity, but they're just as important because of their potential to introduce you to so many of their peers. That's the key."

"Referrals and introductions? Frankly, Victoria, I can't remember the last time a supporter called and wanted to introduce me to someone."

"Referrals and introductions, even from friends, don't magically happen. You have a responsibility to make them happen. There are four referral ground rules."

"Rules? What kind of rules?" asked Oscar.

As Victoria continued, he entered the following into his laptop:

Identifying Stakeholders: Referral Ground Rules

1. Communicate to the referrer that the goal is, first and foremost, to develop a long-term partnership that will impact the mission—not simply to ask for money.

2. Reassure the referrer that identifying prospective stakeholders is the first step—no one will be contacted.

3 List some of the things that will be asked of the prospective stakeholder and share them with the referrer.

4. Above all, make the relationship holder feel comfortable in giving up some of his or her most valuable assets that they've spent a lifetime developing.

"We've asked for referrals countless times at our board meetings," responded Oscar. "But they've never referred many people."

"No, Oscar, you've asked us to give you names of friends and colleagues who would financially support one project or another. That meant our contacts would immediately be asked for money. That's uncomfortable. On the other hand, ask us for potential stakeholders with whom you could develop a long-term partnership with to help our mission: that's more comfortable. Eventually, there will be an ask for money. We all know that. But eventually is not immediately. Feel the difference?"

Oscar thought about it. "I see, Victoria. There is a big difference."

Suddenly, Bob Dailey's referral and introduction to his friends the Jasons flashed into Oscar's mind. *Our goal was to get their $2,500 dinner sponsorship, not develop an ongoing, strong relationship with them. We lost both Bob, a valuable board member, and the Jasons, potentially great supporters.*

"Oscar, over the years, thousands of people have participated in our events and have made contributions. Have you ever identified any of them as potential stakeholders or asked for introductions? That's your responsibility."

"Aren't they already supporters? They come to the dinner or play golf."

"Probably not. They're what I call *undeveloped donors*. Always remember that term. The truth is they support the relationship of the person who asked them to give or attend. At best, they're only supporters of the gala or tournament, not our mission. Most don't have a clue about what we do or who you are. What would happen if the relationship holder is no longer involved with us?"

Suddenly, Oscar realized that it was his responsibility to move those undeveloped donors up the commitment ladder with a productive relationship strategy. It was his responsibility as Executive Director to turn all those contacts into major stakeholders.

"This is probably a good time to take a short break," said Victoria as she stood up. "I have to make a quick call, then we'll talk about how to recruit some of those great prospective stakeholders onto our Partnership Council."

"Good idea. I could use a break about now." Oscar went downstairs outside the building to enjoy a few minutes of sunshine. He couldn't stop thinking about all the new things he was already learning about relationships.

Oscar's Notebook

"Chase money, get a bit,
Chase leadership, score a bigger hit."

◆ Strong leaders want to join groups of their social and business peers, affect change, and produce bigger results.

◆ Build a 20-member Partnership Council as a point of entry and a relationship-building incubator for prospective stakeholders and undeveloped donors. It's a powerful peer leadership team when board or committee involvement is not appropriate.

◆ Five steps to identify new prospective stakeholders are:
1. Build a stakeholder profile
2. Search organization and personal contacts to collect prospective stakeholder names
3. Organize the information in a spreadsheet
4. Evaluate each potential stakeholder
5. Prioritize them

Handcuffed

As they settled in to continue their meeting, Victoria turned to Oscar. "It's time to share the five steps to help you recruit some of those great people you've identified. If you want lots of yes's and a powerful Partnership Council that raises millions, you'll need to learn how to execute these five recruitment steps very well."

Oscar entered the following into his laptop:

To Recruit Prospects into Stakeholders

1. Secure a quality introduction from the relationship holder.
2. Make contact and set the appointment.

3. Conduct a "mission-focused, relationship-
   building" meeting.
4. Connect and uncover the fit.
5. Test close and ask.

It was right about now that Oscar's anxiety really began to accelerate. He interpreted the word "recruitment" as a polite way of saying sales—selling people who made him feel uncomfortable, traveled in different circles, and with whom he had little in common.

Victoria immediately sensed his discomfort. "Oscar, these recruiting steps are usually one of the most challenging things for people to master."

"Why is that?" he asked, trying not to show his anxiety.

"There's probably two reasons: workstyle and fear. First, let's talk about lack of experience because of workstyle. Most Executive Directors spend much of their time on administration, programs, and fundraising. They seldom spend enough time outside their office recruiting prospective stakeholders and developing donors. Recruiting and developing a stakeholder is not about asking for money. Even some development staff are too consumed with event logistics and fundraising administration to do enough stakeholder recruitment and donor management."

At this point, Oscar was wondering how practical Victoria's ideas were. *She has no concept what it's like to run a nonprofit*, he thought.

"Oscar, how often do you, or even Madeline, have breakfast or lunch meetings with prospective and existing stakeholders? How often do you visit them at their home or office? When was the last time you asked someone over to the organization to show them what we're all about? Not to get money or ask for anything, but just to get to know each other better?"

"Perhaps not often enough. But if I did all that, I'd never get any of my real work done."

"If you want to build powerful relationships, things like that become a very important part of your job," said Victoria emphatically. "I think you're going to have to set some new priorities. You'll need to distinguish between what is urgent and what is important."

"What's the difference?"

"Urgent things are responding to e-mails and phone calls. Important things are continuously recruiting new stakeholders and then really getting to know them. Acting on what is important moves you closer to your goals. Constantly reacting to what is urgent often keeps you in the same place. Of course, the choice is always yours."

Oscar knew that parts of his workstyle would have to change. However, how could he change things that felt so comfortable? He was handcuffed to what he knew best.

If I keep to the same routine, I'll keep getting the same results, he said to himself over and over again. So he continued to listen carefully and make detailed notes in his laptop and notebook."

"Here's the second reason that recruiting is such a challenge: most people have a fear of the word sales."

Oscar almost fell out of his chair. "How did you know? I have to admit, I've never liked selling or being sold."

"That's true for most people," said Victoria. "It's certainly true for me, even though I'm in real estate. I overcame my discomfort for selling by un-selling."

"Impossible," laughed Oscar.

"When I un-sell, I think about two things: delivering wins and curiosity. First, let's talk about wins. Selling can be one-sided: one winner and one loser. I un-sell. That means I make sure absolutely everybody wins. Oscar, when people support us, you're giving them so many wins. You're helping them to make a positive impact on so many families. You're helping them to become part of the solution—a contributor. You're helping them to feel positive about what they're doing with their good fortunes and their leadership skills. They're winners as much, if not more, than you are."

"I've never thought about all the wins they could get."

"Next time we meet, we'll talk more about wins. That's our second relationship strategy step. For now, let's discuss curiosity. That's the second way that helps overcome apprehensions about selling."

"Curiosity about what?"

"Curiosity about each prospective stakeholder's job, interests, family. Curiosity about their work and who they are as a person. Some say being curious is intrusive. I don't think that's so if done professionally. People like to talk about themselves and what they do. They appreciate that you're taking an interest in them. I think this might work for you. I've always found you to be extremely curious. It's one of your many strengths. Use it."

Oscar definitely liked people. He always enjoyed finding out more about them. But he always felt it wasn't his place to ask too many questions. He was now beginning to understand ways to develop new comfort zones and make some changes: use more of his strengths. That made him feel so much better.

"Victoria, which of the five recruitment steps do you think is the most difficult to master?"

"Good question, Oscar. Definitely step number three—managing a mission-focused, relationship-building recruitment meeting."

"Why is that?"

"There are probably a couple of reasons. The first reason is that many nonprofit staff only have experience in asking for money. They usually call or visit when they want something. They seldom try to recruit someone to get them involved in the mission. They only try to sell golf foursomes, table sponsors, or "thon" teams. That's not even close to a mission-focused, relationship-building meeting. On the other hand, recruiting prospective stakeholders onto the Partnership Council is almost all mission driven and requires getting to know a little more about each other. That's different, new, and sometimes difficult for many nonprofits to master."

Oscar was trying hard to hold back a big smile. It was beginning to sound like his style of meetings with most of his prospective and existing stakeholders.

"The second reason is that many staff simply don't know how to structure and lead a recruitment meeting. I've experienced that time after time. They come into my office, ask if I know anything about the organization, then talk nonstop for the next thirty to forty minutes about why I should contribute."

"That's usually the way most of us do it. Is there a better way?"

"There certainly is, and it's much more productive. Divide the visit into five different time zones."

"Time zones?" inquired Oscar. "What's that?"

"Since you asked for the meeting, take charge and lead it. That's so important. Create slots of time—time zones—to accomplish different things. Taking charge doesn't mean you do all the talking. It means you get to direct the meeting by asking questions and listening carefully. The person who asks the questions is in charge."

"Are you saying it's okay to lead meetings even with important people like the Worthingtons and Bob? Is this another Victoria okay?"

"Absolutely."

Oscar entered the following into his laptop:

Meeting Time Zones

1. **Create a bonding time zone:** Five to ten minutes to get to know a little about each other professionally and personally.

2. **Develop a question time zone:** Ten minutes asking about each other's business, nonprofit work, interests, etc. A chance to connect, uncover the fit, and discover what you might have in common.

3. **Move into the case statement time zone:** Ten to fifteen minutes explaining the organization's mission and the goals of the Partnership Council.

4. **Go into the test close time zone:** Five minutes asking them open-ended questions about their feelings and perceptions about the mission and Council. Then respond. Also explore the wins further.

5. **If there are enough wins for everyone, move into the ask time zone.** To get a yes, you might have to ask several times in different ways.

Again, Oscar had a flashback to his meetings with the Worthingtons. He mostly talked about the project. In fact, that's all he ever talked about. He asked very few questions. He didn't want to appear nosy or take up what he felt to be too much of their valuable time.

If only I knew then what I know now, perhaps the result would be different!

"There are two other important steps to master when you recruit prospective stakeholders: connect and uncover the fit," said Victoria as she began to finish up their session. "First, personally connect to each other and connect the prospective stakeholder to the mission. That's far more important than giving them all the nuts and bolts about a campaign or event. Second, you should always uncover a personal and/or business fit."

"I always thought the goal was to give them as much information as possible about us and the project so they can decide."

"Oscar, I know your favorite word is yes. Nobody ever says yes based solely on lots of information. What gets people to say yes is the e-factor: emotion—connecting to you and our work."

Again, he thought about it. "Victoria, you're right."

"Once, I attended a Partnership Council recruitment meeting with a cancer organization executive," she explained. "I was a board member. During the bonding and questions, we discovered the prospective stakeholder's child had juvenile diabetes. Before we met, it seemed like the perfect fit—he was a wealthy executive of a large company, influential, and a cancer survivor. But the fight against diabetes was obviously his priority. Nonetheless, we had a very productive meeting. We connected, but there was no personal fit."

"What happened?"

"Eventually, he became a major $7,500-a-year donor and a good advocate for our cause. He never became a Partnership Council member. In fact, we never even asked him to join."

Oscar was definitely feeling more comfortable with the two fundamentals of capturing the right stakeholders: identifying and recruiting. What amazed him most was how much he didn't know and how much more there was to learn about one simple word: relationships, and the path to engage and win over the right stakeholders.

"There are a few more tips which I've gathered over the years," said Victoria. "I think they might help you execute the fundamentals better. Call me, we can discuss them further. But before we leave today, tell me, what do you think are the most helpful things you've learned so far?" Victoria leaned back in her chair, ready to listen.

Oscar took a moment to gather his thoughts. "Use more of my strengths. Take responsibility for developing key relationships. That's an important part of my job. Nothing happens in an organization unless someone is responsible. If I continue to do what I've always done, I'll continue to get what I've always gotten."

"Very well said." Victoria was truly pleased. "Is there anything else?"

"Discovering all the advantages of building a powerful leadership and relationship incubator, our Partnership Council. Accepting what it's going to take to build one: no shortcuts. I know other organizations have done it, so can we," said Oscar excitedly.

"Good. How are you going to capture the right stakeholders?" Victoria wanted to make sure he knew some of the basics.

Oscar moved his laptop so she could see what he had entered on the screen:

To Identify & Recruit New Stakeholders

- Beware of traps: money and power
- Take responsibility for referrals and introductions
- Move contacts up the commitment ladder
- Prioritize urgent things versus important things
- "Unsell" through wins and curiosity
- Take charge and create mission-focused meetings
- Build time zones
- Ask more open-ended questions
- Connect personally with stakeholders
- Connect stakeholders to the mission
- Uncover the fit personally
- Uncover the fit professionally

"Excellent." Victoria knew it wouldn't be as easy as Oscar was anticipating. It would take time and continual practice. She was, however, pleased that Oscar had at least picked up the essence of the fundamentals to the first major step: capturing the right stakeholders.

"Now I want you to go out and put into practice what you've learned. Engage our board. See who they know. Identify some good prospective stakeholders from our volunteers, event sponsors, participants, and donors. Recruit them into a powerful Partnership Council," said Victoria encouragingly. "Let's see what you can do."

They agreed to have conference calls as needed. They also arranged to meet at Victoria's house in six weeks to talk about the second major step: developing win-win relationships.

On his drive home, Oscar thought about his newly acquired knowledge.

Before we began, Victoria was upfront and direct about what it was going to take for me to finally get what I wanted, thought Oscar. *I liked how she encouraged me to use more of my strengths. She wasn't trying to change who I am. She never made me feel that I didn't know how to do my job, only that there were ways to do my job better to reach my goals. She never once lectured or patronized me. It was definitely tough coaching, but she called it the way she saw it. She gave me a ton to work on, but it all makes sense.*

Oscar's Notebook

"Beware of two traps: money and power. Also, move contacts up the commitment ladder."

◆ Prioritize work: urgent vs. important.

◆ Direct and lead compelling recruitment meetings: use time zones, ask open-ended questions, listen, be more curious.

◆ Personally connect with prospective stakeholders, connect them to the mission, and uncover the fit.

◆ Five steps to recruit prospective stakeholders are:
   1. Secure a quality introduction
   2. Make contact and get the appointment
   3. Conduct a "relationship-building, mission-focused" first meeting
   4. Connect and uncover the fit
   5. Test close and ask

Hidden Treasure

As Oscar went about his business over the next couple of days, he began to write down all the things he needed to get started and some of the challenges he might encounter in building his Partnership Council. With each passing hour, his list grew longer and longer—where to identify good prospective stakeholders, who would create and maintain the prospect list, how to evaluate and prioritize them, how to secure referrals, and so on.

By the end of the first few days, his list had already grown to almost four pages, a thousand words long. He had spent many hours putting it together. However, the more he thought about it, the more he knew something was wrong. Something was troubling him.

Early one evening after the staff had left, Oscar sat in his office, thinking about all the things he and Victoria had talked about in their first meeting. In a moment of self-enlightenment, he grabbed the lists that he so carefully prepared, scrunched the pages up into a big ball, and lobbed them into the wastebasket like a superstar. Oscar had arrived at a personal crossroad.

My real challenge boils down to only one word and one word only: me, he said to himself. *I'm the only one who can make it happen.*

Over the next few days, Oscar realized that in order to build those strong relationships, he had three big personal challenges to overcome: be more open, focus on outcomes rather than approval, and get more control.

For starters, he needed to be more open with people—especially with Victoria. *The truth is, I don't ask a lot of questions because I don't want others to ask questions about me. But if I want to build productive partnerships, it has to be a two-way street. How can I expect people to be open if I'm not open with them?*

There was another important personal challenge Oscar needed to work on: focus on the results. He played back in his mind the last meeting with the Worthingtons. Why was he so concerned about whether or not Janice and Ted thought the proposal was good? Why wasn't he more concerned about the outcome? He thought about why he continually asked them, *Is the proposal giving you a good overview?* and *I hope the proposal explains the urgent need.*

Hearing yes to both always gave him great satisfaction. Then, Oscar finally figured it out: he wanted approval on a job well done above all.

The results are what's important, not whether the proposal was perfect and they liked it.

There was a third major breakthrough Oscar realized he needed to make: get more control. He was certainly not the strong, assertive type, but too many times he'd been the loser by not managing outcomes to achieve success. He thought about two things that recently happened.

First, there was Bob Dailey's board resignation meeting. Why was he so upset that Bob never once discussed any of his concerns with him? *It was my responsibility to get more control over the situation. I could have met with him more often one-on-one, asked the right questions, uncovered the wins, established mutual goals, and helped him make the impact he wanted. Everything I didn't do because I thought it would be too intrusive and upset him. I was afraid he'd resign. Well, he resigned anyway.*

He then thought about Janice and Ted Worthington's last phone conversation. *When they turned me down, I could have asked them to help me organize a strong project leadership team, or asked them to help in some other ways. Although they left the door wide open for me, after they said no, I didn't do anything. I thought it would be too pushy. I wonder if it's too late now?*

Suddenly he heard a voice that startled him. "Hello, Oscar. It's time..." said Madeline as she lightly knocked on his office door.

He was so engrossed in his thoughts, he had almost forgotten about his weekly meeting with her. "Come on in. Let's get started." He hadn't prepared for it. He didn't have an agenda. This time, he wasn't quite sure where to start. This was going to be extremely uncomfortable. Would she change her mind and stay, or would she leave?

He began by telling her about Janice and Ted's turndown and about Bob's resignation. Madeline soon had an "I told you so" look on her face, but said nothing. When Oscar briefly filled her in about his meetings with Victoria, she all of a sudden appeared very interested.

"I think it's very important for the future of the organization," he said, "that we have a stronger relationship strategy working. I hope you'll help us."

"Wait a minute, Oscar. As I've already told you, I'm only going to be here a short while longer. Meanwhile, I'm more than happy to help you in any way I can."

Oscar was hoping that their work together over the next couple of weeks would be enough to change her mind.

He continued to explain the Partnership Council in more detail, and the steps to help them identify and recruit the right people.

"Do you think while you're still here, we could uncover some good prospective stakeholders together? We probably have lots of them right under our noses."

"I don't see why not," Madeline said confidently.

"Let's get underway."

* * *

So they began the first step: identifying the right stakeholders. For starters, he and Madeline took a closer look at some of their board members who might have some good connections, just as Victoria had suggested.

Since Madeline's previous job was at Merchant's Bank, she knew some of the right questions to ask about one of their not-too-active board members, Suzanne Brighton. She was also in banking. "Oscar, is Suzanne in commercial or personal lending? Does she work in their private banking, wealth management, or the mortgage division? Is she in an administrative or management position?"

They soon discovered they didn't know as much about Suzanne, personally or professionally, as they had thought. This troubled Oscar greatly.

He then remembered the two traps the Victoria talked about: money and power. "Suzanne could have some very strong contacts. Think about it, Madeline, if she's in private banking, her clients, and possibly some of her friends, could be high net-worth people. If she's in major commercial lending, her contacts would be entrepreneurs, CEOs, COOs, and CFOs. Those are the types of people we want to identify and recruit. We could meet them through Suzanne's introductions."

As they continued examining their board and asking questions about other members, Oscar's thoughts turned to what Victoria had said about workstyle and prioritizing. He kept thinking about what little time he had put into really getting to know those supporters closest to the mission—his board of directors.

Although this was upsetting, he continued to press on. They tried to identify others who might also have strong connections with the right people. Another board member, Brian, was a lawyer at a mid-size firm.

"I wonder what his specialty is?" asked Oscar. He was asking the right questions.

"I remember him telling me he primarily works with contractors and does construction law." She was giving the right answers.

"Then Brian may know developers, builders, suppliers, and maybe even those important architects—all great potential stakeholders for our Partnership Council," said Oscar excitedly.

"I never thought about Brian's contacts," responded Madeline. "He's never been a big donor, nor helped much in our fundraising efforts."

That's the power trap, thought Oscar. "The key is Brian's relationships. They are the types of people who have lots of vendors—good prospective stakeholders for our Partnership Council."

"How do you know so much about that?" she asked

in a surprised tone.

"My older brother happens to be an architect. You would not believe the gifts he gets at Christmas from window, electrical, and many other suppliers. Apparently, architects spec into their plans specific brands and companies, down to the general contractor of the job. Can you imagine the influence architects must have within their industry?"

Madeline was impressed with his newly gained skills. *Who is this person I'm working with?* she thought. *It's not the Oscar that I knew.*

Both he and Madeline were excited about uncovering so many board members who might have relationships with people who would make great Partnership Council members—something they had never done before. Their enthusiasm led them to yet another board member, Ken Anderson, an accountant for a large CPA firm. They both asked the same questions at the same time. "What does he do? What kind of an accountant is he? Who might he know well?"

One of the staff was friends with Ken and his wife. Ken wasn't just another accountant. He headed up his firm's MIS consulting division for a tri-state area.

"More treasure," exclaimed Oscar. "He probably knows lots of the right people for our Partnership Council: CEOs, CFOs, CTOs, CIOs."

One by one, they continued to identify more

potentially great relationship holders. To Oscar's amazement, they discovered six good Partnership Council prospects from within their board. All of them had good connections. They even identified two good prospective stakeholders from their organization's vendors, and three more from their personal contacts. All eleven names were immediately entered into a spreadsheet for safekeeping.

By the end of their meeting, Oscar's excitement slowly gave way to that familiar gut-wrenching feeling in his stomach. He realized more than ever that Madeline would be a valuable partner in helping him build his new relationship strategy. He also better understood her frustrations. *Although I've thought about ways to uncover new stakeholders, I could never figure out exactly how to do it, until today.*

* * *

Over the next few weeks, both Oscar and Madeline continued to identify more Council prospects. This time they focused on their donors and event sponsors. Oscar noticed things he had never seen before, some of which again greatly upset him.

"Although most of our donors contribute less than $150 a year," he said painfully, "except for addresses, it seems we know little about them."

"Oscar, in the past, that's all the information we've needed or wanted. We send donors a thank-you letter, put them on the mail list, then solicit them again. Occasionally, I'd meet with some of them when it was time to ask for money. That's been our development system year after year."

Oscar became more annoyed. "That's not a system. It's more like a fishing expedition using one little pole in the middle of a big ocean. It's not your fault, Madeline."

There was something else that also upset him. Many major contributors and event sponsors seemed to have relationships with their key supporters. Unfortunately, he knew very few of those big contributors. Oscar seldom took the time to meet with any of them, nor asked the relationship holder for introductions to them. He always felt that they were already supporters. What more could be gained?

"Victoria was right again," he said to Madeline. "Many of our contributors are not our supporters—they're undeveloped donors. They support the event or support the person who asked them to give. They're not supporters of our organization or our mission. We've let so many golden opportunities pass us by. Over the years, our so-called development system has probably cost us millions of lost dollars."

"Not to mention how much it cost us in good will," added Madeline. "Imagine how some of our donors must feel about us. They give us money, time after time. They get a form letter thanking them for their efforts, occasionally receive a newsletter, and then we continually ask them for even more of their money. Not too personal."

"That's about to change. We're going to get more control and have a true relationship development system thanks to Victoria's help."

Their painstaking work was slowly beginning to pay off. They discovered lots of leadership treasure right in their own backyard. Through just their donors and event supporters, they identified 16 more prospective stakeholders for the Partnership Council. Their giving levels ranged from $100 to $10,000. They had now identified a total of 27—not earthshaking, but respectable.

It was time to begin recruiting. He needed to call Victoria for a phone-coaching session.

Oscar's Notebook

"Be more open, get more control,
That's part of my new relationship role."

◆ **First,** identify 3 to 6 board members with the
strongest spheres of influence.

◆ **Second,** identify an additional 25 to 35 prospective
stakeholders from undeveloped donors, personal
contacts, existing and/or past contributors, event
sponsors and attendees, and organization vendors.

◆ **Third,** identify the relationship holder for each
prospective stakeholder.

9

The Surprise

"Hello, Victoria, it's Oscar."

"How are things going?"

"I think okay. We're continuing to identify many good Council prospects. I'm about ready to start recruiting. Taking the time to identify the right stakeholders gave me a whole new perspective about our development efforts. No wonder we work so hard trying to raise more money. We're more transactional than I ever thought. I'm surprised we've made the gains we've made."

"Maybe that's why so many nonprofits have lots of small contributors and have difficulty securing major gifts. Oscar, it's easier, more profitable, and far less costly to develop and keep stakeholders by building strong relationships than to look for new ones year after year."

That's exactly what Madeline was saying, he thought. *She continually had to uncover so many new event supporters every single year. That's a lot of pressure and very difficult.*

"How are you coming along with identifying lots of great prospective stakeholders for the Council?"

Oscar filled her in with all the highlights and lowlights. "We've evaluated and prioritized our first 12 out of a total of 27. Six board members, including Suzanne, Brian, Ken, and Bob Dailey, five donors, and the Worthingtons."

Victoria was pleased with their progress. She was even more pleased that Oscar had not given up on Bob and the Worthingtons. He was getting more control. That was very good.

"Here are some things that I think will make your recruitment efforts much more productive," she said. "First, begin by introducing our relationship strategy initiative to the board at one of our meetings. Get their buy-in. Then meet one-on-one with board members Suzanne, Brian, and Ken. Tell them that they are your first group of appointments to discuss building our Partnership Council. You'll be test driving it with them."

Oscar liked starting with his board. He could be more open. He knew them. They were already insiders and he could try out different things. That put far less pressure on him. That was another good Victoria okay.

As Victoria continued, she gave him five tips on how

to make his one-on-one stakeholder recruitment meetings more successful. Oscar entered the following into his laptop:

Recruitment Meeting Tips

1. Set up the meeting at their office or at a breakfast or lunch.
2. Ask for forty-five minutes of their time.
3. Prepare a formal Partnership Council ask letter with both council and family project mission statements.
4. Include bullet points outlining Council membership responsibilities.
5. Share with prospective stakeholders a members to-date list with names and companies.

"Oscar, remember the peer factor? People like to know who's involved. That's very important to them. You can begin with me, your first member!"

Oscar was thrilled about Victoria's commitment. "Thank you so much. I appreciate all your help and support."

"There are two other things that may also be helpful when recruiting. First, look closely at what they have in their offices: awards, pictures, types of accessories, etc. Use these props as conversation openers and a way to uncover some common interests."

"That's a great idea, Victoria. Sometimes I have difficulty talking about things other than our organization."

"Second, uncover the business fit. Remember we talked about that the last time we met?"

"I do."

"When you meet with volunteers like Suzanne from the bank and others, ask some of the following open-ended questions. Make their professional interests also a priority. That builds trust."

Oscar entered the following into his laptop:

Exploring the Business Fit

1. What's your company's philosophy in partnering with nonprofits?
2. Does your company have a partnering strategy?
3. Is your strategy local, regional, or national?
4. At what management level is this strategy discussed and developed within the company?
5. How does your firm link its community service and company image?

"Victoria, that's a lot of things to do in one short meeting, but I'll give it a try."

"Call me after you've met with a few board members."

Oscar, with Madeline's help, then carefully prepared all the Partnership Council and family project support materials Victoria had suggested. They positioned the family center as the first project of the Council. Their golf tournament was repositioned as the Council's "first enterprise" to help financially support the center. Their materials also outlined the project's benefits, giving levels, and financial goals.

Oscar was now fully prepared to capture his first Council member, Suzanne.

* * *

"Thanks for meeting with me on such short notice," said Oscar.

Suzanne had been a $500-a-year donor and board member for almost two years. This was the first time they had met in her office. Most of their time together had been at meetings, on the phone, or communicating through e-mails. The few discussions they did have primarily focused on board business.

"I'm sorry, I don't have much time," said Suzanne as she glanced at her computer screen. "Just tell me more about this new leadership group you mentioned at the last board meeting. What would you like me to do?"

This time, Oscar was determined to be more assertive and direct the meeting. He repeated again and again to himself, *more control and time zones, more control and time zones.*

Suddenly, he noticed some pictures on her bookcase. One of them was taken on a boat fishing. It looked like the same lake his family's cabin was on.

"That picture...do you have a place at Clear Lake?"

"We do, on the north shore," said Suzanne.

"My family and I have a place on the south shore. What do you think of the new restrictions the county wants to impose?"

"My husband and I are not thrilled about it."

Neither was Oscar. They began talking. He discovered they actually did have something in common.

She mentioned her husband was a lawyer with a large firm in town. *Possibly another good Partnership Council prospect*, he thought to himself.

Then Oscar said something he never would have said before. Why he said it, he wasn't quite sure. Maybe it was because she had told him something about her husband, so now he felt obligated to tell her something about his wife. "My wife Debra is head librarian at Evergreen Academy." It was a small, private, prestigious school.

"That's where my oldest daughter goes," exclaimed Suzanne. Again he discovered they had more in common. Now the conversation between them took off, and so did their questions. They talked for nearly twenty minutes, all because of one small fishing picture.

Oscar then asked something he never would have asked before. "Suzanne, as a board member, on a scale of one to ten, how would you rate the impact you feel you've made on our mission?"

Without hesitation, she said, "Honestly, Oscar,

probably only a five at best." She was being overly generous. "I wish I could do much more. I'm not sure where and how. That's why I don't attend many of our meetings or get more involved. Often, it doesn't seem to be the best use of my time."

For once, Oscar appreciated the honesty. He didn't get defensive. It was something he needed to hear in order to make the relationship stronger. He liked Suzanne and wanted her to stay and find her volunteer work rewarding.

"I think all volunteers on nonprofit boards want to make a difference, but many are not quite sure how. I would like to change that for our members."

He then told her all about Victoria's commitment, the new opportunities with the Partnership Council, and the Council's first focus, the family project. Then he sat back, asked her how she felt about it, and listened very carefully to her feedback.

It turned out she had two concerns: time, and how she could help raise the needed funds.

Oscar thought back to what Victoria had said about her Council experiences. "Suzanne, we're projecting a time commitment of about twenty-five hours per year, only a few formal meetings, and one social function. Most of our work together can be done one-on-one."

Suzanne seemed to like what she was hearing so far. He then explored the business fit with her bank. Oscar liked what he was hearing. They were really connecting and there seemed to be a good fit.

"Suzanne, I'll help you every step of the way. Perhaps we can involve certain executives from other departments within your company. If you're comfortable, maybe we can ask some of your clients to join us. They might want to support your efforts." She was in private banking.

"I don't know if I can help raise that kind of money."

"Don't worry about the money. More importantly, I'd like you to think about recommending two or three friends or colleagues who might want to join you on the Council. If we have the right people, I'm confident we'll be successful. Again, I'll partner with you to help recruit them."

Oscar couldn't believe what he was saying. Throughout his entire career, he was trained to do one thing: chase the money first. Always make the ask. That's all that ever mattered.

"Oscar, I think I'm going to need a lot of your help on this."

"We'll work together to make it happen."

Not only did Oscar ask her to join the Council and she accepted, he made a couples ask. He also extended an invitation to her husband to join. After all, their mission centered around families.

"I'm glad we got to know each other more," said Suzanne. "I appreciate you being so candid. We've always needed to have a conversation like this."

"Let's have lunch together. The week after next?"

"I'd like that," she said. They set a time and location.

As they shook hands and said good-bye, he glanced at the clock on the wall. They talked for almost one hour and fifteen minutes. *Not bad for a busy person who didn't have much time to give me,* he thought. *This was so different. I've never experienced a meeting like this before. I actually enjoyed my visit. Best of all, we got the outcomes we both wanted. I wanted her commitment as a Partnership Council member, she wanted a way to be able to help us more.*

* * *

Over the next several weeks, Oscar met with five more board members. He tried to follow the same pattern that was so successful with Suzanne. On one occasion, Victoria joined him. On another, Madeline was part of the team. The results were good, not great. Nonetheless, he slowly became more comfortable. His recruitment skills increased.

Oscar was now about to encounter an even tougher test: recruiting Partnership Council members who were not his board members—prospects who were virtually strangers.

Oscar's Notebook

"Ask lots of questions, see what we share,
Uncover common interests with
donors out there."

◆ Fourth, privately introduce both the relationship
strategy goals and Partnership Council initiative to
one or two of the strongest board leaders. Get their
buy-in.

◆ Fifth, introduce the entire board to the goals and
initiative at a board meeting or retreat. Position one
of the strong board leaders as the lead advocate.

◆ Sixth, in conjunction with a board advocate,
recruit onto the Partnership Council, through
one-on-one meetings, three to six board members
who have strong business and/or personal spheres
of influence.

10

First Contact

It was time once again to call Victoria for their second phone-coaching session.

"Hello, Victoria. It's Oscar. Do you have a few minutes?"

"Sure. Let's talk. How are you doing on your recruitment meetings?"

"Pretty good so far. I've met with six board members. Four said yes, Suzanne, Brian, Ken and Mary."

"That's very good, Oscar. You're probably now ready to recruit two other groups of prospective stakeholders. The first are donors you hardly know. The second are referrals from others who have never had contact with you or the organization."

"I'm as ready as I'll ever be."

"Then it's time to talk about two important recruitment steps: how to secure solid introductions and get the appointments."

"I thought the introduction was getting the appointment?"

"It's always easier if the relationship holder sets the appointment and participates. That's not what typically happens. A good introduction usually means the relationship holder has opened the door to the prospective stakeholder. Now he or she will take your call. Here are some ways that might help you get those good introductions."

Oscar entered the following into his laptop:

Recruitment: The Introduction

1. Explain more about the Partnership Council to the relationship holder.
2. Ask the referrer for more information about the prospective stakeholder.
3. Uncover how he or she knows the prospective stakeholder.
4. Describe to the referrer exactly what you'll be asking of the contact.
5. Suggest they make the introduction by phone or e-mail. An in-person introduction is always better.
6. Provide the referrer with some brief talking points

      and a suggested e-mail about the purpose of
the introduction.

7. Request the referrer tell the contact you'll be calling to schedule a thirty to forty-five minute meeting.
8. Encourage the referrer to participate in the recruitment meeting.

"That's a very long list of to do's just to meet someone," laughed Oscar.

"These people aren't just someone. A person's relationships are one of their most valuable assets. They're golden. They've spent a lifetime developing them. The one and only way to effectively make contact is through a good introduction."

"It still seems like a lot of extra work."

"Oscar, if you have a lot of time on your hands, enjoy chasing down prospective stakeholders forever, and are extremely good at persuading strangers to give you an appointment, you don't have to do any of this."

"I understand, Victoria. But after they make the introduction, then what do I say to get the appointment?"

"Your first phone contact is like the in-office visit, only much shorter. Same challenges: control and time zones. Do a good job here, your recruitment meeting goes so much smoother and becomes more productive."

"I thought I'm just calling to set up an appointment. A few minutes and I'm off the phone. There's more to it?"

"Yes, Oscar, there certainly is. A good appointment setting call can take ten to fifteen minutes. It's another challenging step to master. They're busy people. They don't want or need to meet with you. Besides, they're conditioned to expect your visit is nothing more than a thinly disguised attempt to immediately ask for money. That's why they'll always try to avoid you."

"So what can I do?"

As Victoria gave him some valuable tips on how to get the appointment once the introduction is made, Oscar entered the following into his laptop:

Recruitment: Setting the Appointment

1. Try to bond immediately.
2. Get him or her to talk more than you.
3. Ask the prospective stakeholder where and how they know the relationship holder.
4. Use the information given by the relationship holder to engage them in a short conversation.
5. Briefly tell the prospective stakeholder the purpose of the visit. "We thought you'd be interested in hearing more about a key leadership team we're forming with folks like you to impact our mission."
6. Always use your time zones, but make them much shorter.

"Oscar, mastering the fundamentals of the introduction, first contact, and setting the appointment takes time. Don't get discouraged. Good luck. Let me know if I can help you further."

Victoria had once again given Oscar some more difficult things to master. Together, he and Madeline carefully prepared written talking points and a sample e-mail to help all the relationship holders make their introductions. As is so typical with busy volunteers, Oscar soon discovered, getting them to follow through would also be another ongoing challenge.

* * *

An important introduction was soon made to George Singleton, an insurance executive and a two-year, $10,000 per event, golf tournament sponsor. George, through his company, was a major donor because of his relationship with Tony, one of the tournament co-chairs.

Oscar always knew George was a key contributor— truly an undeveloped donor— that he needed to meet and get to know, but he never did. For over two years, he left the relationship responsibility in the hands of Tony. A $10,000-a-year donor was rare. It was a major gift to Oscar's organization. But he never handled it as if it was all that special. Now trying to set an appointment with George for the first time was not only going to be difficult—it was going to be embarrassing.

Within a week thereafter, Oscar finally got George on the telephone to schedule their meeting.

"Hello, George, this is Oscar Shelton, Executive Director. I was introduced to you at our golf tournament, the event Tony chairs. I hope you enjoyed it."

"I met many people there. The tournament was fine. What can I do for you?"

"First, thank you again for your sponsorship. It has helped so many families here in our community. Tony suggested I call you. I know we should have touched base long before this. I'd like to set an appointment to meet."

"Tony called me. I don't remember exactly why you wanted to meet. If it's about next year's sponsorship, that's going to depend on our new budget. I'll let Tony know."

"I wasn't calling about your tournament sponsorship." He could sense George was becoming impatient. "By the way, where do you know Tony from?"

"He's a longtime client of our firm and a close friend. I'm very busy right now, how can I help you?"

If there ever was a time to get more control, thought Oscar, *now is as good a time as any.*

"George, Tony and I thought you might be interested in hearing more about a new leadership team we're putting together with select business and community leaders like yourself. People who are interested in making a major impact on families who need help. If you like what you hear, you may want to consider joining us."

This was a difficult first telephone call for Oscar. He was doing the best he could. He continued to try to get more control and use his time zones.

By now, Oscar's persistence was beginning to turn George's impatience into a major irritation. "After all these years, why do you suddenly want to meet? Frankly, I donate to your tournament because it's important to Tony. I wanted to support his efforts. In over two years, I've received a couple of thank-you letters and numerous requests to contribute more. I still don't know very much about your organization nor exactly what you do."

Oscar became very upset. He knew George had every reason to feel the way he did. Most donors would not be so forthright. They would think it, but never say it. He thought it was about time to be more open.

"You and your company are one of our major contributors. $10,000 a year is a great deal of money and very important to our work. We're making a strong effort to get to know all of our supporters better. It's something we haven't done a very good job of in the past. That's the purpose of my call—to set an appointment to meet you."

"I appreciate your candor, Oscar. I'm so busy right now. If you're calling about getting me involved on another committee, I don't think I'm interested."

"I understand. Nonetheless, I'd like to meet with you for about thirty to forty minutes to tell you about how we've put your contribution to work helping families in our community. My visit has little to do with your golf sponsorship."

"You're welcome to come over, but I don't think you're going to convince me differently."

Oscar accepted the challenge. They set an appointment to meet at George's office in a couple of weeks. After all these years, Oscar was finally going to try to build a relationship with one of his most important donors.

At first, Oscar felt his efforts with George were a waste of time. After all, he said that he had no interest in getting involved further. Then he realized it was just the opposite. Oscar was finally taking more control over the future of an important contributor. He made George his responsibility, not Tony's. Strong relationships take time and trust. This was a good first step with a major donor whom he didn't know well—a key contributor who had received little in return from the organization for over two years.

Oscar continued to set more recruitment appointments. He met with many types of prospective stakeholders. A few referrals were unfamiliar with the organization, others were undeveloped donors. Some were big contributors, most were small. He gradually became more comfortable and gained more control as he had with George. It was beginning to pay off.

Oscar's Notebook

"A good introduction is needed for all,
So valuable prospects will take the call."

◆ Seventh, meet with relationship holder of each
  prospective stakeholder to secure a quality
  introduction.

◆ Eighth, contact the prospective stakeholder, set the
  recruitment appointment, and use this opportunity
  to begin to share and uncover things in common.

◆ Ninth, get more control over the first contact. Use
  time zones, be patient, ask open-ended questions,
  listen, be curious, make the ask for the meeting
  several times in different ways.

11

Last Chances

Almost six weeks had passed since the launch of Oscar's new relationship strategy. He had now secured six Partnership Council members and scheduled eight more recruitment meetings. However, there were still three more important things to do before he met with Victoria again: a final meeting with Madeline, a Partnership Council forum to identify more Council prospects, and a follow-up visit with the Worthingtons.

Madeline's forty-five days were up. At their final meeting, he made one last chance effort to get her to stay.

"You've been a great partner in helping to launch our relationship strategy," said Oscar. "You've got some good skills in this area. It seems I've underutilized your talents."

"Oscar, it's been very rewarding working like this over the past weeks."

"You know I want you to stay. I've given it a lot of thought. Perhaps you should have more donor management responsibilities to develop major gifts and less responsibility on fundraising administration."

"What do you mean?" Madeline inquired.

"Developing donors, managing our supporters, and building a major giving program are very different than handling all the logistical details of a fundraising event or campaign. Each is important, but none more important than building stronger relationships with our stakeholders."

"Oscar, we both know that building strong relationships takes time. Lots of time. Where am I going to find it? It sounds like you're just piling on another layer of work."

"Not at all. I'm going to shift and prioritize."

"I don't understand."

"There's two key parts to a successful fundraising program: donor management and fundraising administration," replied Oscar. "You share an assistant with another staff. Your assistant, with the help from the volunteers, can take more direct responsibility for the many time-consuming administration details. Then she can report back to you. Although those details produce great events, they don't build relationships. Ultimately, it's strong relationships that raise big money. That's a priority."

"This is an entirely new approach. Tell me more."

"Madeline, with this restructuring, you'll have much more time with committee and Council members, key donors, and select event participants. Now you can focus on developing stronger relationships and turning those relationships into bigger things. You won't be spending endless hours deciding on the dinner entertainment and decorations, or the golf tee gifts and trophies. Your job evaluation and performance objectives will now be centered around your relationship-building successes. What do you think?"

Madeline knew Oscar would try to make one last effort to get her to stay. However, this was so different from anything she had ever expected. "Oscar, is this another experiment, or are you serious?"

"Very serious. It's a priority. Developing a relationship strategy is essential. You'd be a valuable partner."

There was dead silence. It was so quiet, you could hear a pin drop. Madeline was thinking it over.

She had been talking to her old employer, plus a few other people to see what might be available. But she very much liked the work of helping families. She also liked the idea of donor management and major gifts much more than fundraising administration.

"Oscar, I've seen a lot of new things around here start, then slowly fizzle out. Helping families is important. I also like your plans. If you're all right with it, perhaps I could give it three more months and see how it works for both of us."

Oscar thought about it for a moment. "I think I can work with that," he replied. Although it was not exactly what he wanted, he was still relieved. A big burden had been temporarily lifted off his shoulders.

* * *

With one major hurdle overcome, Oscar and Madeline began preparing for their first Partnership Council meeting. They wanted members to help them identify more Partnership Council prospects. Although they had tried to get referrals from their board in the past, the results were always poor. They were determined that this time, things would be different. Once again, they called Victoria for their third phone-coaching session.

"Victoria, Madeline and I are on a speaker phone in the conference room. We need to talk to you about how to get referrals and introductions from our new Partnership Council members. Our first meeting is coming up shortly."

"Before we begin," said Victoria, "Madeline, I'm very pleased that you're giving it three more months. Oscar told me yesterday. You'll be a big asset."

"Thank you for the vote of confidence," Madeline said excitedly.

"Victoria, we've always struggled in getting good

referrals," lamented Oscar. "How can we make it work better?"

"First, you have to get members to attend. I'll send an e-mail announcing the purpose, our goal, the date, and location," replied Victoria. "They can RSVP to Anne, my assistant."

"That'll definitely get their attention," said Madeline.

"Here are eight things you can do," suggested Victoria, "to get some good referrals this time at our meeting."

As she explained some ways to help them uncover more prospective stakeholder referrals from supporters, Oscar entered the following into his laptop:

Identifying Referrals

1. Communicate to all participants that the goal is to identify Council prospects, not to uncover donors to ask for money.
2. Provide participants with a profile of a good prospective stakeholder.
3. Emphasize that nobody is going to rush off and call their contacts.
4. Explain the next steps: evaluating and prioritizing each name. If there's interest, each relationship holder will be asked to make an introduction.
5. List the prospective stakeholder's name, company, and, most importantly, job title in a spreadsheet.

6. Identify who holds the relationship with each prospect and, if possible, indicate how they know him or her.
7. Identify only people with whom participants can comfortably make an introduction.
8. Prepare materials to help each relationship holder make his or her introductions.

"Those are some good ideas," said Oscar. "I wish I knew about them before. Again, things might have turned out differently."

"There's one more suggestion that's very important," continued Victoria. "At the meeting, start your search by focusing on industry groups. You might ask them, 'Do you know any executives in real estate, title, mortgage companies, or banks? Do you know any executives in agri-business, co-ops, farm equipment, or transporation?' Always keep your search in industry groups. That makes it much easier for participants to think about people and come up with more names."

"Thanks again, Victoria, for some great phone coaching," said Oscar.

* * *

As best they could, he and Madeline then implemented many of Victoria's tips. Their first Partnership Council meeting produced 16 good prospective stakeholders in less than one hour. Victoria suggested four of the names. Not as many as they had hoped for, but respectable nonetheless for a first-time effort.

After the meeting, Victoria told them she was more than pleased with the members' enthusiasm and the overall results.

There was still one last thing Oscar had to do before his second meeting at Victoria's house: meet with the Worthingtons. He wasn't looking forward to it. This was his last chance to get them involved.

* * *

Everything Oscar had learned was about to be put to the test. He was seated in one of the Worthingtons' smaller conference rooms awaiting Janice and Ted's arrival. Minutes seemed like hours as he nervously tapped his foot on a colorful area rug.

"What conversation openers?" he mumbled to himself. "There's nothing here but a table, four chairs, and a clock on the wall. I can't remember a thing they had in their offices. How can I start my bonding time zone?"

"Hello, Oscar. It's nice to see you again," said Janice as she walked in alone.

"Thanks for the time. Where's Ted?"

"He's tied up in a meeting across town. He won't be able to attend. We can continue on without him."

Out of curiosity, Oscar asked, "While I was waiting, I noticed this colorful rug. Where did you get it? It's very nice."

"Santa Fe, New Mexico, one of my favorite places to visit," she said enthusiastically.

Amazingly, that's all it took. Janice jumped in and told Oscar all about how they had met the weaver and loved her work. Oscar and his wife Debra also liked Santa Fe—the Indian arts, shops, museums, and, of course, skiing. Unexpectedly, he and Janice shared some of their New Mexico experiences for almost ten minutes.

Now that things had loosened up a bit, Oscar asked, "Last time we talked, you briefly mentioned your other nonprofit work. What other organizations are you and Ted involved with?" That was a good follow-up question from their last conversation.

"Unfortunately, too many. The hospital foundation, Boys and Girls Club, the food bank, several arts groups, and, of course, our church and their efforts to help people in our community."

"It sounds as if you have a full plate. Janice, I'm curious, why would you and Ted be interested in getting involved with us?" Oscar asked a good, open-ended question. He was taking more control of the meeting.

"The work you do and the help you provide is unique among nonprofits. We're not looking to become board members. That's a little premature. We are looking to make a difference in some way."

"Are you still interested?" Another excellent question. He needed to hear the answer in order to effectively shape their conversation and build their relationship.

"I don't know. I have to say, we were more than a little disappointed in your reaction when we told you we were unable to help fund the family project."

Oscar now knew he definitely didn't handle that situation as best he could. Was there any way he could turn it around without opening old wounds?

"Why were you disappointed?" he hesitantly asked. Yet another good open-ended question he didn't shy away from. His question allowed her to express her feelings. Although the answer might be painful, Oscar knew in order to build a relationship, he had to know her thoughts.

"It appeared as if you were only interested in our $50,000. Although Ted specifically told you we hoped this would be the beginning of a long relationship, you said nothing at the time. We didn't hear back from you until now."

Janice was open and honest in her feelings. Oscar also wanted to be more open with his. "You're right. I apologize. Our relationships with donors and prospective supporters like yourself is something we've recently been working hard to change. That's why I asked to meet with you."

"Unfortunately, it seems to be all about the money with too many nonprofits," interjected Janice.

Oscar was startled. "Maybe it's because of our driving desire to raise more funds so we can serve even more families. I know that's no excuse. We're working very hard to build better relationships with community leaders like you and Ted."

"That's good to hear."

"Until now," continued Oscar, "except for becoming a board member or working on an event committee, we've never really had a point of entry for new supporters—a position in the organization where you could grow with us."

"As I said, we're not interested in becoming board members, nor do we have the time or interest in helping organize yet another event. What did you have in mind?"

Oscar then went on to explain all about his new Partnership Council and how the family project was positioned as the Council's first enterprise for members to support the mission. He even made an attempt to uncover some mutual wins.

It was obvious to Oscar that she appreciated his openness. Janice listened closely. She had been part of a similar leadership team like this before and knew the great things a strong group of supporters could accomplish.

Oscar was now about to begin his test close time zone. "How would you and Ted feel about bringing your time, talents, and leadership to the table and joining us as Council members?" This was another good open-ended question.

Janice immediately started asking Oscar all kinds of specifics about his plans for the Council: who was going to be on it, who the chairs and vice chairs might be, and what the members' responsibilities would be.

Once again, he remembered what Victoria had told him about how a Partnership Council is structured. "Since you and Ted seem to have a deep interest in the project, how would you feel about a co-chair position as a couple, and perhaps asking another couple to join you?" Another open-ended test close question to uncover her thoughts.

"That's a big step. We almost weren't going to take this meeting today. Now you want us to be a co-chair? I don't think that's likely to happen."

"Becoming part of the Council is one way that you and Ted can guide the success of the family center. Janice, your leadership can make a big difference." Good follow up test close.

"Oscar, I don't know you that well. It seems you're somewhat different from the last time we met. I appreciate you being more open. You've given me a chance to express my thoughts. I have a much better perspective about the organization and your goals. I'll tell you what, I'll talk to Ted about it. We'll get back to you."

"Janice, thanks for considering joining the Council. I look forward to hearing from you. Whether you chair the Council or not, I'd be very grateful to have your time, talents, and leadership."

As far as Oscar was concerned, their meeting was a big success. Getting the Worthingtons to even think about joining the Council was a win. *We now know a little more about each other. What could have turned into a huge disaster a few months ago without Victoria's coaching now has the possibility of turning into something great,* Oscar said to himself as he thanked her and left the office.

* * *

While driving through late afternoon traffic, he thought about all he had learned and all he had achieved in just a few short weeks. His new workstyle still felt uncomfortable, but it had taken him so far. Although the results were not earthshaking, it was nonetheless working. Every time he put into practice the things he learned from Victoria about building stronger relationships, there was always something good coming from it. People responded positively. For the first time, he was not getting what he had usually gotten—he was getting so much more.

At long last, there was also the possibility of having a true development director—a position he had urged the board to fund for many years. Madeline was staying for at least three more months. That was good.

Oscar was also becoming much better at identifying potentially great stakeholders. Not only was he starting to get some good referrals and introductions, he was starting to connect the dots and becoming much better at evaluating a stakeholder's different resources. Oscar was more open with people and getting so much better at gaining more control.

He was turning potentially negative situations into positive outcomes.

There were now ten influential business and community leaders on his Partnership Council. He was finally building a powerful leadership team, not chasing money as he had always done for so many years.

Oscar's Notebook

"Ask open-ended questions, that is a must,
Then listen, ask more, and build their trust."

◆ Tenth, schedule and lead the first Partnership
Council meeting once 8 stakeholders have been
recruited. Referrals to members' vendors, colleagues,
and friends should be a key agenda item.

◆ Assign one, and only one, lead staff to build,
manage, and lead the Partnership Council. All
Council members should have the same relationship
manager from within the organization.

◆ Distinguish between staff's donor development
responsibilities versus staff's fundraising
administration responsibilities. This is critical when
building a strong relationship strategy.

12

Shortcuts

Like many people, Oscar still loved figuring out shortcuts. No matter how hard he tried, he could never resist that urge. He was now about to demonstrate his proficiency at always finding a faster and easier way of doing things.

What a fantastic Tudor home, he said to himself as he turned into Victoria's long, tree-lined driveway. It was time for their second meeting.

He gathered up his papers and took his laptop out of his trunk and walked up the steps to the doorway. "Good afternoon, Oscar. I heard you driving up. Come in."

As they walked through the living room towards a bright, sunlit study, Oscar couldn't help but notice that Victoria's home looked as if it came out of the magazine pages of *Architectural Digest*.

"We can spread ourselves around this table. Before we start, I've got some cold lemonade for us on the backyard patio. Let's go out there and catch up."

Victoria didn't merely have a backyard—she had a park. Meandering paths bordered by colorful flowers wove endlessly through tall, majestic oak trees.

"Tell me, how are you feeling about all of this so far?" she asked as she leaned back and sipped her tall glass of lemonade.

Although Victoria was his board chair, he knew it was important to be as open as he could to make it all work. After all, she was his coach.

"I have to be honest, Victoria. Most of this seems to be going well. But it still doesn't seem normal. It still feels somewhat uncomfortable."

"You're probably right. I wouldn't expect this to feel natural to you yet. Give it more time. Oscar, imagine learning how to write with your other hand. When you concentrate so hard on every move, it takes more of your time and energy. Soon, you'll develop that new comfort zone we've talked about. You'll be running on automatic."

Oscar couldn't wait until that time arrived. "You're probably right. I've always been a little impatient."

"Any other thoughts before we go inside and begin?"

"Victoria, I've been thinking about how to save time. I think we can really streamline some of this."

"Such as?" Although Victoria didn't know exactly what his suggestions might be, she could easily see what was coming and summarize them in two words: *shortcuts* and *delegate*.

"Let's form a Council sub-committee," said Oscar excitedly. "They can be responsible for recruiting more members. Madeline could work with them. Also, we could write letters to supporters to join our Partnership Council. What do you think? Good ideas, aren't they?"

Knowing people the way she did, Oscar was living up to most of her expectations. "Oscar, as Executive Director, the single most important thing you can do to help grow the organization is to build strong relationships with the right people. That's your responsibility, not our volunteers'. Relationships are personal. It's something you can't delegate. Only you can initially build those key relationships. And it starts with your very first face-to-face recruitment meeting."

Oscar then thought about how he managed George's relationship, his major $10,000-a-year golf tournament sponsor. He didn't. He completely delegated his responsibility to Tony, who chaired the golf committee. Suddenly he felt helpless. *What would happen to George's contribution if Tony leaves?* he thought to himself.

Nonetheless, in typical Oscar fashion, he continued to defend his shortcuts. "Isn't a peer volunteer better able to convince others to join our Partnership Council or become a donor?"

"Do you really think that's the best way to build your relationships? Besides, most volunteers simply don't have the time nor the expertise. You're lucky if they find an hour to join you on one recruitment appointment. They're all experts in their own professions, not development. You're the expert, they aren't."

Like a dog on a bone, Oscar would not give up. "What if—"

Victoria finally stopped him in his tracks. "Oscar, you can take any shortcuts you want. However, there are no shortcuts that I've seen work. If you knew exactly how to build strong relationships with the right people, you would already have gotten all the things you've always wanted."

Oscar took a moment to think about it. "Victoria, you're probably right. All these years, I've tried it my way. So far, I haven't gotten what I've wanted. If it is to be, it is up to me."

"Well said. Let's fill up our glasses and go back into the study. We're going to talk about how to grow and keep our stakeholders."

Although Oscar barely had a chance to explain all of his wonderful ideas, he knew Victoria was right. *I was the king of shortcuts*, he chuckled to himself as they walked back into the house to begin their second coaching session.

Oscar's Notebook

"Relationship builders never leave it to fate,
It's much too important to delegate."

◆ The single most important thing I can do to grow
our programs is to build strong relationships
with the right people. That's my responsibility, not
our volunteers'.

◆ Relationships are personal. It's something I can't
pass off to others.

◆ Staff are the development experts, not the volunteer.
If it is to be, it is up to me.

13

The Big Payoff

As Oscar plugged in his laptop to begin their second coaching session, he glanced around Victoria's oak-paneled study. He noticed three walls covered with hundreds of books of all kinds. They were neatly tucked into finely crafted, floor to ceiling bookcases. On the other wall was a massive stone fireplace. The room and her whole house were, to say the least, very impressive.

I wonder how her strong relationships played a part in her success? he thought to himself.

"Once you've captured the right stakeholder," she began, "within weeks, it's time to begin executing our second major step: develop a win-win relationship. Some call it cultivation, but it's much more. If you can identify and deliver stakeholder wins, this is the road to your big payoff."

"How so?" asked Oscar curiously.

"Once a prospect says yes to your ask, on a relationship scale of one to four, you're probably at a one with your new stakeholder. The goal is to move the relationship to a three or four. That turns $150 into $10,000."

"What's the trick?" Oscar was anxious to know.

"There's no trick to it. It's just that some people skip over this step, others have difficulty executing it."

"What do you mean?" inquired Oscar.

"They get the commitment or check and run, only to return when it's time to ask again. Many don't stick around to develop a win-win relationship. Then organizations wonder why it's so tough to consistently raise big money."

"Lately, I've thought a lot about that, too," said Oscar, embarrassed.

"Stakeholders want wins," continued Victoria. "Our supporters' wins are non-monetary, so they're much harder to uncover than traditional monetary wins. Not only do stakeholders want wins, they want lots of them, and they want them continuously. That's not easy to do."

"We go the extra mile to thank and recognize donors. We're always showing our appreciation. We listen to their ideas."

"Those wins are all important, but stakeholders usually want more. Good relationship builders do two things here, and do them well. They identify lots of stakeholder wins. Second, they continuously deliver those wins."

"Are you saying we're not giving enough wins to our supporters?"

"There are probably many wins they want that you're not giving them. Otherwise, we'd have lots of happy, motivated donors constantly giving us more and more of their time and money. Oscar, you and I know that's not happening enough."

Once again, Oscar felt that familiar knot in the pit of his stomach. *Bob was unhappy. The Worthingtons are unhappy. Even our board member Suzanne and our major gift donor George are unhappy,* he thought to himself. *How many more supporters like this do we have?*

"Exactly what wins do they want that they're not getting?" Oscar inquired. He was becoming frustrated.

"Our stakeholders' wins are often difficult to define. Before we talk about ways to identify and deliver them, let's first look at two types of wins: personal and business."

As Victoria read some examples from a list she had, Oscar entered the following into his laptop:

Stakeholder Wins

Personal Wins
- Sense of accomplishment
- Making an impact
- Recognition/anonymity

- ◆ Personal networking
- ◆ Sense of affiliation
- ◆ Participating in solutions
- ◆ Socialization
- ◆ Being the leader
- ◆ Control

Business Wins

- ◆ Good corporate citizen
- ◆ Positive public relations
- ◆ Enhanced media coverage
- ◆ Increased visibility in the community and marketplace
- ◆ Increased sales
- ◆ Improved *esprit de corps* between managers and employees

Oscar was surprised there were so many kinds of wins. "How do I know which ones they want?"

"Let's talk about how to identify wins. That's always a puzzle. The food industry obsessed over that for years with their ready-to-eat meals. Finally, they had a revelation. They discovered that some people want to do a bit—just a little bit—of actual cooking. They want to feel as if they were making it from scratch, doing something wholesome for their families and themselves. Popular products like Hamburger Helper, unlike microwave meals, give some people a sense of accomplishment. They're doing just enough—adding, stirring, browning, etc."

"What's that have to do with us?"

"Actually a great deal," added Victoria. "Identifying wins is not always easy. Perhaps some of our donors may want a stronger feeling of accomplishment. Writing a check isn't enough. They may want to do a little more of their own cooking, so to speak."

"That's why we have so many different ways to volunteer."

"Volunteering is not a win. It's a way to get a win. Bob and Suzanne volunteered. They still didn't get their wins. Not fulfilling a stakeholders' wins is one of the single biggest reasons why organizations have difficulty building strong donor relationships and keeping supporters."

"You not only want me to manage an organization, but you also want me to make supporters' wins come true?" said Oscar jokingly. "That's asking a lot."

"When you fulfill stakeholders' wins, great things happen. If you don't continuously uncover and deliver wins, I promise you, someone else will. Most won't tell you that they're unhappy. They'll just pull up stakes and take their big pot of resources elsewhere."

"I don't want to be nosy or get too personal trying to figure out what they want," said Oscar.

"You don't have to be. There are three things that good relationship builders do to identify their stakeholder's wins."

Oscar entered the following into his laptop:

Three Steps to Identify Wins

1. Get to know your stakeholder
2. Create a stakeholder mosaic
3. Develop high impact touches

"Oscar, what's troubling you all of a sudden?"

"They're our donors. I'm not looking for more friends. Some of this feels too intrusive."

"Let's take a closer look at those three things that help to identify wins. First, get to know your stakeholders. In a relationship strategy, donors are always people first, stakeholders second. That means get to know your supporters as people, not just as contributors. It doesn't mean become best friends with every donor. That's unrealistic. Look beyond his or her role as a stakeholder. Get to know them as an individual."

"That seems reasonable enough," said Oscar as he began to feel a little more comfortable.

"You would think so, but for many, it's not that easy. Some people don't know how to get to know people."

"I appreciate your Yogi Berra-like statement, but doesn't everybody know how?"

"Apparently not. Some people have relationship blockers."

"What's a relationship blocker?" asked Oscar. "Are

they unfriendly?"

"Not at all. I've met many people who have difficulty getting to know others who are very amicable and likable. They may be shy or somewhat closed. Others may feel more comfortable keeping business separate from their personal life. While still others may feel they shouldn't pry. Then do you know what happens?"

"Not really," replied Oscar.

"Their style with supporters becomes all about the work and less about getting to know them as a person. They seldom ask questions. They constantly struggle to move up the relationship scale."

Immediately, Oscar could see some of those blockers in himself. "Let's say someone is like that. What can they do?"

As Victoria gave him some ways to conquer them, Oscar entered the following into his laptop:

To Overcome Relationship Blockers:

1. Make the relationship the goal. Not the sale of a golf team, gala table, or the naming brick on the walkway. It's the relationship that helps you get more of what you want.

2. Develop a healthy curiosity about people. Learn more about them as a neighbor, parent, and businessperson.

3. Ask lots of questions. Let them do the talking.

4. Most importantly, be more open and vulnerable.

"That fourth point," he said. "'More open' I can understand, but 'vulnerable'? That's absolutely the last thing I want to be with a donor."

"Actually, Oscar, it's probably the first. It means be open about your strengths and weaknesses. Don't be defensive or judgmental. Ask for their ideas and help. Vulnerability shows honesty, and honesty builds trust. Trust is the fundamental bonding agent in every good relationship."

"But vulnerability shows that you don't know what you're doing or have confidence."

"Just the opposite. Several years ago, the Director of Development of the Mentoring Center came to visit me. I was on the board. She wanted introductions to a couple of my friends. She was very open in saying that neither she nor the organization was used to meeting such prominent people. She felt somewhat uncomfortable. Her vulnerability showed honesty. I trusted her. Our relationship grew stronger. I made the introductions, set the appointments, and attended both meetings. One of my friends eventually became a major $20,000 donor."

Oscar was beginning to understand. "Recently," he said, "I stuck my neck way out. I was more open and vulnerable than usual, but it felt okay. I told both George and

Janice that building stronger donor relationships was something that we hadn't done a very good job of in the past. They understood and I think they appreciated me being open about it. I could feel things slowly change for the better. Is that what you mean by being more vulnerable?"

"Exactly. You took a risk. You were upfront and truthful. Your openness and vulnerability showed honesty about yourself and the organization. You built trust."

"Maybe I'll try being more vulnerable more often."

"You'll experience a big difference. Before we talk about the second thing good relationship builders do to identify wins, creating a stakeholder mosaic by sharing and collecting information about each other, I think it's time for a short break."

"Definitely," said Oscar as his mind continued to spin. "I could use one about now."

Oscar's Notebook

"First, make a donor's wins come true,
Then they'll share good fortunes with you."

◆ Execute the second relationship-building step; develop win-win relationships within weeks after the stakeholder says yes.

◆ Two fundamentals to develop win-win relationships are:
1. Identify lots of stakeholder wins
2. Deliver the wins continuously

◆ The first of three steps to identify a stakeholder's wins is to get to know the stakeholder as a person first, a contributor second.

14

Out on a Limb

Upon returning to Victoria's study to continue their meeting about how to create a stakeholder mosaic or picture, Oscar began to feel uneasy. "Do I now have to become a Sherlock Holmes? If so, I don't think I can do this part."

"It's not about snooping or prying. We're talking about uncovering the kinds of information about your stakeholder that people naturally want to know about each other when forming a productive partnership. It starts from the very first meeting and continues throughout the entire relationship."

"It's not my nature to keep files about people."

"We all do it, Oscar—especially if the person is important to us. For friends, we keep mental files. At work, we keep written files. It's impossible to remember everything about our key stakeholders."

"How do you suggest uncovering this information?" Oscar asked hesitantly.

"Ask lots of open-ended questions. Share things about yourself."

"Like what?"

As Victoria gave him some suggestions, Oscar made the following notes:

Identifying Wins: Create a Stakeholder Mosaic

1. Are you originally from here?
2. Tell me a little more about your company.
3. My wife Debra is a librarian at Evergreen Academy.

    And your husband/wife?
4. My son Terry is now 17, and he's off to State University next year. How about you?
5. I've been with the organization as Executive Director for 8 years. And yourself?

"There are two types of information that create a mosaic or picture about people:" continued Victoria, "personal and professional. There are some important basics you should know about each key stakeholder."

"Such as?" inquired Oscar. He then entered the following into his laptop as she continued:

Identifying Wins: Build a Stakeholder Mosaic

I. PERSONAL

A. Family
- Martial status
- Names and ages of children
- Spouse's name, occupation, title and company
- Years in the community/hometown

B. Experience
- Former employers
- Past nonprofit commitments
- Schools and education
- Current nonprofit commitments

C. Other
- Relationship to the mission and/or the organization
- Favorite hobbies, sports, and interests
- Achievements

II. PROFESSIONAL

A. Business
- Types of products/services
- Key executives' names and titles

◆ Competitors

◆ Charitable giving sources/history

◆ Number of employees

◆ Marketing and sales methods

◆ Ownership/locations

◆ Vendor types

B. Job

◆ Title/responsibilities

◆ Length of employment

If these are just the basics, Oscar thought to himself, *I've got a long way to go to learn more about my stakeholders.*

"Finally, let's look at the third and last way good relationship builders identify stakeholder wins: they develop high impact touches."

"Victoria, there are so many ways we already stay in contact with supporters: newsletters, e-mail updates, special invitations, volunteer meetings, etc. What more is there?"

"Those are important, but they're not enough. There are two kinds of touches: general and personal. General touches such as newsletters and e-mails make a low emotional impact, a small impression, and are soon forgotten. Personal touches, such as a thank-you card from one of our families or you and your stakeholder enjoying a ballgame together, make a high emotional impact, a big impression, and are long remembered."

"If you're suggesting asking donors over to my house for a barbecue as a personal touch, that's not going to happen."

Oscar was truly a master at keeping his work and personal life very separate. "Since relationships are personal, Oscar, some of your touches must also be personal. Make them interesting and provide a benefit to the stakeholder. Tailor some touches to their interests so that he or she wants to spend time with you."

"Our resources are limited. How can I possibly do that?"

"If you and Madeline execute the following plan, you'll immediately create over 200 high-impact touches each year."

Oscar entered Victoria's personal touch plan into his laptop as follows:

Identifying Wins: Build a Stakeholder Touch Plan

1. Select twenty "A" category stakeholders (your Partnership Council and others with great potential), plus ten "B" category stakeholders (those whose commitments you want to build). Over the year, touch the "A"s four times, the "B"s twice.

2. Make each touch one-on-one, not in a group setting. Half of the touches should occur someplace

other than his or her office: breakfasts, lunches, after work, etc.

3. Deliver a stakeholder benefit in at least half of the touches: a relaxing coffee break at Starbucks, a couples dinner, a tour of a family program, a thank-you plaque to display, a small gift based on their interests or hobbies.

4. Focus half the conversation on getting to know each other. Don't discuss organization business. Ask lots of questions. Share things about yourself.

5. Tailor the touches. One touch each year should focus on the stakeholder's hobbies or interests: a sporting event, fishing, golf, tennis, bicycling, wine tasting, lecture, etc. Be sure to also tailor one touch each year so that the stakeholder personally experiences your mission in action and/or meets one of the organization's beneficiaries.

"Good ideas, Victoria, but where's the budget for all of that?"

"There are many ways to make high impact touches that cost virtually nothing."

"Those are magic words," said Oscar excitedly. "How?"

"Some organizations have what I call a 'goody closet.' Volunteers help fill it with all kinds of donated things: extra wine from the gala, golf and tennis balls from their tournaments, tickets to plays and sporting events, restaurant and day spa coupons, and so on. Everything is acquired free from supporters and their contacts. It's all reserved for and shared exclusively with key stakeholders—not used to raise a little money from a drawing or auction."

Immediately, Oscar thought about his volunteers and all the things they could possibly donate.

"Before discussing how to deliver wins," said Victoria, "let's stretch our feet and go outside to the patio. We can refill our glasses."

* * *

As they overlooked the majestic gardens, Victoria wanted to make sure that Oscar understood the basics so far. "Oscar, what are two things you'll need to do to develop win-win relationships?"

"First, identify stakeholder wins. Second, continuously deliver those wins," he quickly responded.

"Very good. How do good relationship builders identify wins?"

"First, get to know the stakeholder. Second, create a personal mosaic. Third, develop high-impact touches," Oscar answered without hesitation.

"Excellent. Tell me, what do you think are the most helpful things that you've learned so far?"

"Be more open and vulnerable, ask more open-ended

questions, gather and share information, and develop a high-impact touch plan," he said confidently.

Victoria was pleased. "Before leaving today, let's go back inside and talk about the second thing you'll need to do, and do well, to develop win-win relationships: continuously deliver those wins."

Again, Oscar wasn't sure he could comfortably do that. "Victoria, isn't this a bit risky?" he said as they walked back to the study.

"Not if you avoid two traps: the win must be appropriate and well-timed. That's why the single most important thing about delivering wins is knowing what you and your stakeholder have in common—your shared ideas, values, ambitions, and goals. It avoids offending one another. It avoids killing the relationship."

"I still feel that I'm sticking my neck way out on a limb," said Oscar apprehensively as he sat down in the study and moved his laptop closer to him. "This could be very risky if I deliver wins they don't want."

"It doesn't have to be," said Victoria reassuringly, as she settled back in a big leather chair next to the fireplace. "Within weeks after joining the Mentoring Center's Partnership Council, the Executive Director and I got together for lunch. He asked some direct, open-ended questions and listened carefully. These questions not only helped him uncover more of my wins, they ensured the wins he delivered would be appropriate and well-timed. He asked me, what I call, some insurance questions."

Oscar entered the following into his laptop:

Delivery Wins: Ask "Insurance" Questions

1. What attracts you to our organization?
2. What are some of your expectations?
3. What outcomes would you like to see?
4. How do you see yourself helping us achieve our goals?
5. What were the most and least desirable things about some of your other nonprofit involvement?

Oscar then scrolled through his laptop and looked at some of the wins Victoria had suggested. "What if the win is recognition? What more could I do?"

"Write a thank-you letter to the supporter's company about the valuable contribution the volunteer's time has made in helping families. In your newspaper thank-you ad after an event, not only list the contributing company, list the supporter's name who helped make it happen."

"Business networking?" asked Oscar. He wanted more examples of wins he could deliver.

"Ask your supporter who he or she does business with. A stakeholder who is an executive in a bank's trust or wealth management department might want to join you at a meeting with a lawyer or accountant."

"Victoria, if control or being the leader is a win, what

can I do?"

"Position the volunteer as your mentor. Schedule time for one-on-one updates, ask questions, seek advice, create strategies, and build action plans together. Save chair or vice chair committee positions for people who not only can get the job done, but who also want to lead."

Oscar continued to ask about other wins and Victoria continued to offer easy, practical ways that he and the organization could deliver them. Once again, Oscar's mind was spinning with questions and ideas.

"Does this give you enough to think about in building your strong win-win relationships?" she asked.

"More than enough," he said as he finished writing a few things in his small notebook. "When are we going to meet again and talk about our third and final step? Turning relationships into productive outcomes?"

Victoria flipped through her calendar. "How about five weeks from this Thursday at your office?"

"That's good. Victoria, thanks so much for all your help. This has been great."

"You're welcome. I'm glad you're pleased."

During Oscar's drive home, he felt more than pleased—he felt re-energized. It was as if he had discovered chambers of buried treasure—riches that would help him accomplish some of his organization's long-desired dreams.

Oscar's Notebook

"High-impact touches four times each year
Closes the gap, makes the goal so near."

◆ The second step to identify a stakeholder's wins is to build a personal and professional mosaic about the supporter.

◆ The third step to identify a stakeholder's wins is to execute a series of yearly, one-on-one, high-impact stakeholder touches.

◆ Two steps to deliver a stakeholder's wins are:
   1. Uncover shared ideas, values, and goals
   2. Ensure the wins are appropriate and well-timed

15

Secrets Revealed

Oscar's enthusiasm continued. After returning to his office the following Monday morning, he gathered all his notes and entered the following into his laptop:

Develop Win-Win Relationships

Fundamental #1: Identify stakeholder wins

A. Get to know your stakeholder

- Learn more about him or her as a person first, stakeholder second
- Be more open and vulnerable

B. Create a stakeholder mosaic

- Share information about yourself
- Collect information about the stakeholder

C. Execute high impact touches
- ◆ Create more personal touches
- ◆ Build a touch plan

Fundamental #2: Continuously deliver wins

A. Uncover shared ideas, values, and goals
- ◆ Avoid relationship killers
- ◆ Ask direct "insurance" questions

B. Execute appropriate and well-timed wins
- ◆ Explore wins with the stakeholder
- ◆ Listen carefully for clues to identify what's appropriate

C. Employ reasonable organizational and personal resources

Over the next couple of weeks, Oscar continued to identify and recruit new leadership for his Partnership Council. He gained more confidence and became more comfortable with each effort. However, building the win-win relationship was more difficult than he thought. He had yet to make one single relationship-building appointment with Council members or other stakeholders.

Slowly, he was becoming more and more frustrated. In true Oscar fashion, he wanted to start with exactly the right person in the right situation so he could assured everything would go perfectly.

"Hi, Oscar," said Madeline as she greeted him late one afternoon in the coffee room. "How was your second meeting with Victoria?"

"Excellent. And to say the least, eye-opening." They sat down at a small kitchen table next to the refrigerator in the coffee room and he told her more about it.

"How's this part of it going so far?" she inquired.

"I'm trying to decide which stakeholders to meet first."

Madeline knew Oscar, and she knew him well. She took his answer to mean he hadn't done much so far in building those win-win relationships. Although Oscar was a good Executive Director and a very supportive boss, he was definitely a perfectionist and somewhat slow to try new things.

"Perhaps you should start with board members who are also on the Council," said Madeline. "That worked well before. I'll be glad to join you."

He thought about it only for a moment. "Good idea. I'll call them and set appointments."

That's all it took to get win-win relationships rolling.

Since Madeline knew most of the board members, having her join him made it much more comfortable.

As the weeks passed, Oscar and Madeline threw themselves into trying to build win-win relationships with several key stakeholders. At first, it seemed odd to him. He was so used to always asking for money and talking all about the organization. He struggled to follow Victoria's recommendations.

However, with each stakeholder visit, he gained more confidence. *These meetings are sometimes like a Cracker Jack box,* he laughingly thought to himself. *They're full of surprises. I had no idea Ken's sister is on the school board. I never knew one of our supporters and I graduated from the same university, just a year apart. Victoria was right, getting to know stakeholders as people first can be fun and personally rewarding.*

* * *

Although things were working out fairly well for Oscar, he felt he wasn't quite connecting with some of his new stakeholders. He was more curious and was getting better at asking more open-ended questions, but he felt there was something missing. It was definitely time for another one of Victoria's phone-coaching sessions.

"Hello, Victoria, it's Oscar. How are you?"

"Fine, thanks. What can I do for you?"

"That chemistry with stakeholders...sometimes I feel I'm not connecting. I have an important meeting with George and I'm concerned about it."

"Making that connection is critical. Are you sincerely trying to build the relationship," asked Victoria, "or in the back of your mind, is it more about the money?"

"Both," answered Oscar without hesitating. "Part of my job is fundraising. Isn't that what it's all about?"

"You're right. You need to raise money and lots of it.

But first you need to connect with your stakeholders. That should be your goal. Maybe you're still making them feel as if it's all about their financial contribution."

"I always start off my meetings with light conversation before I get down to business," said Oscar confidently.

"Are you putting the other person's needs first and putting yours second?"

"Of course I am. They don't want to waste their time. Don't supporters ever expect me to talk about us?"

"They do, but if you want to build stronger relationships, make your needs simply the wallpaper in the scene."

"I don't understand what you mean."

"Oscar, as you build your relationship and learn more about each other, opportunities will naturally surface that will be a good fit. Then everyone will get his or her wants and wins."

"What am I supposed to talk to them about? Their last fishing trip?"

"That's a good start. Keep digging to uncover things that you have in common. Discover at least two significant interests, goals, or values you share. If you don't, you haven't done a good job in moving the relationship to the next level."

Oscar thought about it. *Victoria's right. Little chemistry, not much in common. Lots of chemistry, a great deal in common.*

"The single most important thing you can do to build

a powerful relationship," emphasized Victoria, "is to uncover things you share. When two people see things in the world the same way, they feel they can trust each other. Try it with George."

"That'll be difficult. He's really put off with us. We're meeting, but he's not interested in getting involved further. Is it too late?" asked Oscar in a tone of desperation.

"It's never too late if you make the relationship, not the money, your primary goal."

"We sort of have a relationship. We've met several times at the tournaments. I've sent him many thank-you letters. Recently, we've even talked on the phone. We're not strangers."

"That's true, you're not. You have an awareness of each other. You don't have a relationship. An awareness and a relationship are very different."

Oscar felt that familiar knot in the pit of his stomach return. *Then I probably have lots of awarenesses and not enough strong relationships—that's trouble.*

"Good relationship builders know exactly where they stand with stakeholders on the relationship scale," said Victoria. "That keeps you on track and avoids problems."

"Perhaps that's why George is irritated," said Oscar hesitantly. "Since he gave $10,000, I assumed we had some sort of a relationship and he'd be interested in learning more about us."

"You can't rewind the clock, but you can start to build

your relationship. You may discover many things in common."

"I doubt it, but I'll try."

"Oscar, a strong relationship transcends many problems. It allows someone to forgive and overlook many things."

"I hope you're right. I've got so much riding on George," said Oscar nervously.

"Continuing to focus on his $10,000 makes your visit all about you and the money, not about him and building a relationship. That'll immediately become transparent. You'll lose."

"How do I know where I stand in the relationship?" Oscar was concerned.

"Measure it against this relationship scale."

As Victoria outlined the four relationship levels, Oscar entered the following into his laptop:

Our Relationship Scale

Level I. Professional Zone:

Knowledge of each other's professional roles. The result of the first one-on-one contact. Little knowledge of each other as a person.

Level II. Individual Zone:

Heightened knowledge of each other as a person beyond professional roles. The result of second and third one-on-one, high-impact touches. Uncovering one or two common interests.

Level III. Win Zone:

Delivering lots of mutual wins. The result of on-going, high-impact touches. Sharing things outside business. Uncovering more common interests, values, and goals. Some professional and social interaction.

Level IV. Partnership Zone:

Building and acting upon common ideas and opportunities together. The result of continued high-impact touches. High degree of trust. Frequent professional and social interaction.

"Oscar, a good relationship takes time to develop—usually at least 6 to 12 months. It seldom occurs through a couple of meetings or a single round of golf, no matter how well things go."

"Sometimes I feel it's difficult to gauge how things are really going. People always want to be nice to each other."

"It's easier than you think," said Victoria with a smile. "Remember an enjoyable meeting? There was a solid exchange of feelings, opinions, and perspectives. Deep down inside, you felt things were going well."

Slowly, a smile also appeared on Oscar's face. He thought about his first lunch with Victoria at the diner. They seemed to click.

"You're right again," said Oscar, amazed. "I even enjoyed my recent meetings with Suzanne, our board member, and with Janice Worthington. We shared things. I felt the chemistry."

"Exactly. Now you're in the relationship game."

"Victoria, I have one question before I meet with George. I've learned so many new things about relationships. What do you think are the three most important secrets to better relationships with people?"

Victoria paused for a moment. "I'm so glad you asked," she said as she thought about it more. "I don't think they're secrets in the truest sense. If we had to take all of our work together and list the three most important things you could do to build stronger relationships, they would be..."

Oscar quickly entered the following into his laptop:

Three Relationship-Building Secrets

1. **Be more curious**
2. **Put the other person first, your needs second**
3. **Uncover common interests, values, and goals**

"You're right, Victoria. I agree. Those are the three most important things. Thanks. Our time on the phone today has really helped."

"My pleasure. I'll see you at your office a week from this Thursday. We'll talk about the third and final step—turning relationships into productive outcomes. Good luck with George."

Oscar's Notebook

*"If you continue to focus on the
major gift sale,
You'll never move up the relationship scale."*

A. Three steps to build stakeholder chemistry
and connect:

1. Uncover things in common. Discover at least
two shared interests, ambitions, values,
and/or goals.

2. Make the relationship, not the money, the
primary goal.

3. Know exactly where you stand with a
stakeholder on the relationship scale.

16

Amazing Turnaround

Before he knew it, the day of the big meeting with George finally arrived. Oscar was determined to try out some of the things he had learned.

Decked out in his best blue blazer, neatly pressed grey slacks, and a crisp white dress shirt with a deep burgundy tie, Oscar nervously entered the tomb of the unknown donor. As George greeted him in the reception area, he immediately sensed that George was not overly enthusiastic about their meeting. *Perhaps going to a relaxed setting—neutral turf—might help*, he thought to himself.

"It's 3:30. How about a quick break?" asked Oscar. "I thought we might go down to the Starbucks in the lobby, have coffee, and talk." That was a good suggestion. He was already giving George a win.

"That's fine," responded George. "I only have a few minutes. I've been here since 7 o'clock in the morning. It's been a long day."

It was obvious to Oscar that George just wanted to get the meeting over with as soon as possible.

As they rode the elevator downstairs, Oscar then asked a good follow-up question. "Do you usually come in early?"

"Most of the time. We built a home on the West side and I like to avoid the traffic."

Oscar was about to uncover something else they had in common. "I'm curious…was building your own home a challenge?" Oscar's follow-up, open-ended question showed he was listening, interested, and concerned.

After ordering, they sat down in two big, executive leather chairs across from each other. George then began to tell Oscar some of the trials and tribulations of home building. Oscar continued to carefully listen and ask more follow-up questions based on George's responses. Most importantly, he didn't talk business.

"I know what you went through," said Oscar. "Last year, my wife Debra and I remodeled our family's cabin on Clear Lake. That was a small job in comparison, but no walk in the park. I can understand your challenges." Mentioning his wife by name took Oscar out of the professional role and moved him into the personal role.

George seemed more relaxed. His attitude towards Oscar was slowly changing. "Beth and I were just talking about that area the other night—buying a second home up there. It would be a great place to spend time with our two grandchildren. What's it like?"

Oscar told him all about life at the lake. He asked questions about George's grandchildren, and they shared experiences about some of their mutual hobbies. To his surprise, they had a lot in common. Time seemed to fly by.

"I asked for a half-hour," said Oscar. "It's been almost that. Perhaps we should continue this another time?" Oscar showed he was a person of his word. George could trust him.

"Oscar, it seems that you and I have a lot to talk about after all. I have nothing scheduled for the rest of the day. We'll just get interrupted at my office. Let's finish up here."

Oscar was shocked. *What a difference thirty minutes had made. This is a different George,* he thought.

He was experiencing something new with a potentially difficult donor. They were connecting. He could sense some chemistry between them. Best of all, he was actually enjoying the visit.

They talked for another twenty minutes. Oscar explored both the personal and business fit by asking lots of open-ended questions. George also asked lots of questions about the organization. They both found each other's jobs interesting.

"If, and when, I get out of insurance," said George,

"I've thought about going into a not-for-profit like yours. It's a chance to make a difference."

Oscar chuckled. He couldn't resist spending a few minutes sharing some of an Executive Director's challenges. He made himself more open and vulnerable.

"George, it was great meeting with you."

"Likewise. Don't forget to e-mail me the names of those two real estate people you recommend up at the lake."

"I'll do it tomorrow. Let's have lunch together in a couple of weeks."

"I look forward to it. Call me and we'll set it up."

* * *

On his way home, Oscar wasn't riding in his car—he was riding on air. He had never experienced anything like this before. He was so excited, he immediately called Victoria.

"I'm glad I reached you before you left the office. Victoria, it worked! There was a complete turnaround. I focused on him, not on me or my needs. This time, I listened—I really listened. I only talked about 40% of the time. We uncovered so much common ground. I didn't think that was possible with someone like George."

"Isn't this way so much better?"

"Light years better. Ironically, it seems when I get off business and get into the relationship, that's the most powerful thing I can do. I felt, for the first time, that he and I connected."

"You've just discovered the best kept business secret in town. Best of all, you've just experienced it. How does it feel?"

"Like I won the Super Bowl of relationship-building. And it didn't feel put-on or false. I genuinely like George. He's a great guy after all."

"Your sincerity and interest was obvious to him and he responded accordingly. I'm excited for you. See you on Thursday. We'll talk about our third and last step: how to comfortably turn those great relationships into productive outcomes. Congratulations."

Oscar kept the relationship going. He called George to see how his home search was progressing. They had lunch together several times. He and his wife Debra got together with George and Beth at the cabin one Saturday afternoon when George was at the lake looking for property.

Oscar even invited George over to the office, introduced him to some of the staff, and showed him the mission in action.

He never once asked George about the $10,000 tournament sponsorship. There was no need to. Oscar would soon experience another shock with him. This time, it would be one of an even greater magnitude.

Oscar's Notebook

"If you want to be shocked,
amazed, and aghast,
Look at a stakeholder as a person at last."

◆ Get off business, get into the relationship—that is
the single most powerful thing I can do.

◆ Talk only about 40% of the time.

◆ Listen—really listen.

◆ Focus on the stakeholder, not on personal wants.

17

Unleashing the Genie

The day of Oscar's final coaching meeting with Victoria had arrived. As Oscar escorted her into his office, she immediately sensed something was troubling him.

"What's the matter, Oscar?" she asked in her best coach's voice. "You don't seem yourself."

"Today's topic is asking people whom I've gotten to know well for money. That always makes me feel uncomfortable."

"It's more about ways to naturally bring to the surface opportunities within our organization that are a good fit for you and for your stakeholder—the art of asking others to share some things that will make a difference. It's also about uncovering some of their resources to produce tangible, productive outcomes to affect our mission."

"I don't ever want someone to feel obligated.."

"Sometimes that's a common feeling."

"It's more than sometimes with me," chimed Oscar.

"It's not about being manipulative or tricky. It's the natural next step that happens between two people who have a strong win-win relationship. It's that connection that motivates them. They really want to step up and help."

"What about taking advantage of the relationship?"

"People do more business with people they know well," said Victoria as she tried to make him feel more comfortable. "Decisions aren't always based solely on the merits of what a contribution will accomplish. Oscar, why did the Worthingtons say no? Was it because of the lack of need for a family center? Was it because of a poor proposal?"

"Of course not. They wanted to help organizations with whom they're strongly connected."

"That's my point. The Worthingtons, like most people, say yes and want to help because there's a strong relationship. Then they want you to present win opportunities to them that'll be a good fit. Have you thought about our work together?"

"Constantly. Why do you ask me that now?" inquired Oscar curiously.

"We've spent hours together. I've given you lots of my time, energy, and expertise. Do you know why?"

Oscar was startled by the question. He fumbled

through his mind trying to give what he thought to be the right answer. "Because you're on the board?" he said hesitantly.

"Not exactly. Chairs don't have to do all of this. Most don't. It's because our mission is important and I respect and like you. You've got great potential. Over the years, we've built a relationship. That's why I'm more than happy to give you all the help I can."

Oscar was speechless. He finally understood it. "You're right, Victoria. Great things naturally happen when there's a strong connection."

"Always remember that. You'll know when it feels right to present some opportunities to George—they'll be good fits for both of you."

"I hope so. I wouldn't want to jeopardize our relationship."

Victoria couldn't help but chuckle to herself. "You won't, if you learn how to execute well the following two fundamentals that turn relationships into exciting results."

Oscar entered the following into his laptop:

To Turn Relationships into Productive Outcomes

1. Build two to three mutual goals with
   the stakeholder.
2. Coach the stakeholder to help them reach
   their goals.

"Most stakeholders have far more than money to offer," continued Victoria. "They have two powerful circles of influence: personal and business. Uncover them. That's how you turn relationships into productive outcomes."

"We already do that," said Oscar somewhat defensively. "My friend Jerry Singleton is the local manager for Pepsi and donates beverages to many of our events. That saves us about $800 a year."

"Think bigger. Much bigger. What's more important: saving a few hundred dollars on soda or building relationships with some of Jerry's colleagues who could help you raise hundreds of thousands of dollars?"

"That seems impossible, although I wish that would happen," said Oscar laughingly.

"It can. Stakeholders like Jerry can be your genie in the bottle. He'll help you fulfill many wishes. Think of his great contacts with supermarket and convenience store executives. Imagine if you could get a few introductions and then build relationships. You could raise tens of thousands of dollars with them and their grocery suppliers. I've personally seen that happen."

"That's certainly the way I'd like things to work, but they haven't."

"Until now," said Victoria with a big smile. "I know you could easily change that if you follow these three steps to build mutual goals."

Oscar made another entry into his laptop:

Build Mutual Goals

1. Think out of the box. Explore a stakeholder's two powerful circles of influence: first, identify five or six of his or her personal resources and relationships that would make an impact; second, identify five or six of his or her business resources and relationships.

2. Evaluate each resource and relationship. Select three or four of them that would be difficult to get and would produce the biggest impact.

3. Meet one-on-one with the stakeholder, explore the opportunities. Then mutually agree on a total of two or three that he or she will comfortably share.

"Oscar, that's how you unleash the genie within great stakeholders. Although you might uncover lots of things you want from him or her, they'll usually grant you only three wishes. So select carefully."

Suddenly, he thought about his recruitment meeting and follow-up lunch with Suzanne. She had so many great, untapped resources and relationships. "Victoria, there's one catch, however. Volunteers often make promises they don't keep."

"That's why the second fundamental, your expert

coaching, is so critical," she emphasized.

"I always follow up."

"Good coaching doesn't mean to continually call them week after week to check up on them. That's annoying and frustrating. Most want to come through, but they don't know exactly how. Look at all the things you and Madeline are doing with our supporters to make contact with new prospective stakeholders."

"We're working hard at it," said Oscar. "We're moving the relationship holders through all those referral and introduction steps."

"Exactly. The same thing applies here. To be a great coach to your stakeholder, you'll need to do the following three things."

Oscar made his final entry into his laptop:

Coach

1. List the four or five steps needed to make each one of the stakeholder's commitments happen. Also list any support materials necessary to successfully execute each step.

2. Using both the organization's and stakeholder's resources and skills, first produce the important support materials, then execute each step.

3. Flex your coaching style to accommodate stakeholder's workstyle, personality, skills, and resources.

"That's good coaching," said Victoria. "Consistent coaching always turns stakeholder promises into great results."

"Again, you've given me so much to think about and work on. It's all comfortably falling into place."

"Oscar, remember: you're the fund development expert, not them."

Oscar's Notebook

"Stakeholders possess more than money they say,
Uncover them, build goals, coach
each step of the way."

◆ A strong connection makes a stakeholder want to step up and help more.

◆ People do more business with people they know well—decisions aren't based solely on merit or need.

◆ Two fundamentals that turn relationships into productive outcomes are:
  1. Build mutual goals
  2. Coach

◆ Three steps that build mutual goals are:
  1. Explore circles of influence
  2. Evaluate and prioritize
  3. Mutually agree on those resources the stakeholder will share

◆ Three steps to effective coaching are:
  1. Build an action plan for each commitment
  2. Examine resources and skills, and produce support materials
  3. Flex your coaching styles

18

Dreams Come True

Oscar continued to put into play all the things he had learned. Most of it went well. Some didn't. He never gave up and always continued to try.

He and George learned more and more about each other. Although George didn't talk much about who he knew, Oscar discovered that he was well-connected in town. Some of the city's top business executives were George's clients and friends.

During one of their lunches, it happened. Deep down inside, Oscar suddenly felt the time was right to present George some opportunities to get involved. "George, I've been thinking. There may be lots of ways that you and I could help so many families. How do you feel about doing something together?" Oscar asked a good, open-ended, test-close question.

At first, George was startled. They had seldom discussed things about the organization. But by now, George felt he really wanted to do more to help Oscar.

"I'm not sure what you mean. What did you have in mind?"

Since George didn't give him an answer, Oscar wisely asked him again. This time in another way. "What do you think about us somehow partnering together to help solve this crisis with our city's families?" Another good, open-ended, test-close question.

There was absolute silence that seemed to go on for hours. Oscar sat back, said nothing, and patiently waited for George's response.

"Oscar, recently, I read an article in the newspaper about a family like the ones you help. It also got me thinking. I'm glad you asked. I'd like to do something together. Financially, I've given about all I can give."

"I wasn't thinking about more money." Oscar couldn't believe what he had just said. Neither could George. Oscar then asked another excellent open-ended follow-up question. "What are your thoughts about getting together some people who you know who might feel the same way we do about this problem? They may be interested in partnering with us." He wanted to meet some of George's friends, clients, colleagues, and vendors.

This time, George thought about it for only a moment. "That sounds do-able, depending on what you come up with."

"What do you think about hosting a small mission briefing? Perhaps 10 to 12 couples—friends and neighbors— at your house. Maybe we could do an executive breakfast briefing at your club for about 12 business associates?"

George was silent. He was thinking it through. "How will all this work?"

"We'll introduce them to our organization and what we're doing to help solve the problem," responded Oscar quickly. "I promise, there won't be any ask for money. If there's further interest in the organization or the Partnership Council, I'll meet with them later, one-on-one. Our staff will help with all the logistics."

George was relieved to hear that Oscar would not immediately be asking his friends for money. "That sounds like a good possibility. Let me discuss it with my office and Beth. I'll get back to you in a few days."

Of course, George and Beth couldn't say no to both ideas. They were happy to help.

Oscar and Madeline coached them every step of the way. Together with George and his wife, they worked out invitation lists to ensure that the right people would attend. Madeline prepared a short, written agenda with talking points and a brief Power Point presentation. She and other staff also arranged for a family to speak, produced name badges, collected the RSVPs, coordinated the hospitality, and afterwards, sent thank-you cards.

The results weren't good—they were earth-shattering. George and his wife, along with eight new influential people, ultimately joined the Partnership Council from different major businesses throughout town. It was only the beginning.

During the next several months, Oscar built strong relationships with each of them—the same way as he did with George. Most supported the family project with a $10,000 golf tournament foursome. In turn, they and other Council members, through friends and vendors, filled the field with $10,000 teams and helped get a $50,000 title sponsor. The tournament netted over $350,000!

Eventually, a Partnership Council member introduced Oscar to a very special couple who ultimately donated a small, commercially zoned house—the new family center! Another member, with Oscar's help, approached two of her vendors. They became the Center's name sponsors.

* * *

An incredible year had quickly passed. The organization had finally reached the next level. Oscar could hardly contain his excitement and appreciation as he updated Victoria during lunch once again at his favorite diner. They sat at the very same table where it all began.

"Victoria, thank you so much for helping me. So many aspects of my life have dramatically improved. I couldn't have done it without your coaching. But there's one question I've always been meaning to ask you: how do you know so much about relationship-building?"

There was a long moment of silence. Victoria smiled. "I'm pleased you finally asked. Oscar, I came from a family of modest means. My father died when I was 13. Mother did the best she could raising three children. Early on, I learned the value of building strong relationships as an important core life skill. That changed my whole life. I was offered good after-school jobs and got great recommendations from teachers and friends for some scholarships and entry into better schools. To this day, the single most valuable thing I have is my great relationships. I treasure them more than anything else."

"Unfortunately," said Oscar, "building strong relationships is something they don't teach us in school. I wish they did."

"I wish they did, too. Oscar, I've gotten so much out of our relationship—probably more than you did. There's just one more request."

"What is it?" he asked hesitantly.

"Let's have lunch together…again!"

Oscar let out a huge laugh. "Victoria, that's something I'll always continue to do."

Oscar's Notebook

"Building relationships are key life skills,
They help you climb over those difficult hills."

◆ Some of the most valuable assets a stakeholder can give are usually things other than money.

◆ Ask for something that is difficult to get and something that will make a big impact—most stakeholders only grant three wishes.

◆ Make an open-ended, test-close ask before asking for something specific.

Epilogue

The following year brought many changes—mostly good ones, some not so good. Oscar reconnected with Bob Dailey, his premier ex-board member who had abruptly resigned. He tried to revive the relationship, but couldn't. There was too much water under the bridge.

There was another disappointment: Madeline left the organization, but continued to help people in need. She was offered the program director position at a small, local foundation. Although Oscar was saddened by her leaving, he knew it was an excellent opportunity. They kept in contact and remained friends.

Most of all, he felt a big void when Victoria stepped down as board chair. Her two-year term came to a close. Although she remained active for several more years, it wasn't quite the same. Their friendship continued, however.

Overall, the year brought more highlights than disappointments. Janice Worthington joined the Partnership Council and eventually became one of the Council's co-chairs. Her growth in the organization paralleled George's. She helped Oscar recruit many new, influential business and community leaders as Partnership Council members. Several eventually became board members and major gift donors, along with herself. They in turn brought aboard their relationships, who also became Council members and major contributors. The cycle continued.

There were also a few surprises. Jerry Singleton, his longtime friend from Pepsi, eventually introduced him to several of his supermarket and convenience store contacts. Oscar developed good relationships with two of them. Through their efforts, along with Pepsi and some of their other grocery vendors, they annually raise over $250,000.

Suzanne, Oscar's once-not-too-active, $500-a-year donor and board member, became reconnected. She introduced Oscar to many of her friends and high net worth clients. Several became long-term major donors. A couple of them, like she and her husband, joined the Partnership Council and also became major contributors. Suzanne even got her bank financially involved with a yearly $10,000 contribution.

Oscar and the organization are doing very well. They opened the new family center and have plans for a second facility across town. Oscar also started an endowment— something he wanted to do for many years.

Oscar continues to always build relationships. That's a big part of his job now. Most work out well, some don't. His staff has greatly expanded. There are now two full-time development professionals and an events coordinator.

A couple of times a year, he and Victoria still meet for lunch at his favorite diner. As usual, they sit at their famous table. Oscar has changed his lunching habits. Now he only eats lunch alone once every few weeks. Some old habits are hard to break.

Throughout all of Oscar's successes, he never lost sight of what made it all possible: relationships. He now raises more money than he could ever have imagined. He has less stress, finds his work easier and far more rewarding, and is having a lot more fun in life. He's finally getting more of what he's always wanted.

Today, if you walk into Oscar's office and look to the left, you'll see a big sign on a corkboard that says:

- ◆ **BE MORE CURIOUS**
- ◆ **PUT THE OTHER PERSON FIRST, YOUR NEEDS SECOND**
- ◆ **UNCOVER COMMON INTERESTS, VALUES, AND GOALS**

THE END

Let's Have Lunch Together

The Whole Book on a Page

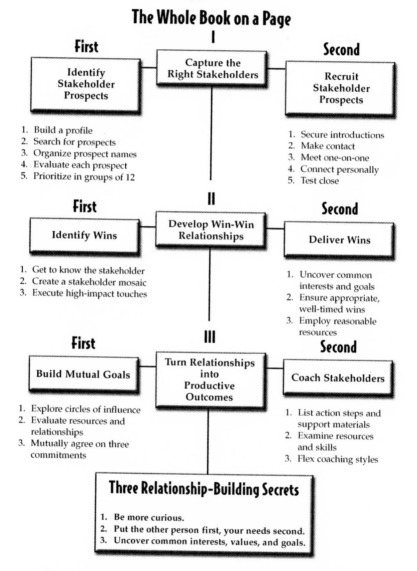

I

Capture the Right Stakeholders

First

Identify Stakeholder Prospects

1. Build a profile
2. Search for prospects
3. Organize prospect names
4. Evaluate each prospect
5. Prioritize in groups of 12

Second

Recruit Stakeholder Prospects

1. Secure introductions
2. Make contact
3. Meet one-on-one
4. Connect personally
5. Test close

II

Develop Win-Win Relationships

First

Identify Wins

1. Get to know the stakeholder
2. Create a stakeholder mosaic
3. Execute high-impact touches

Second

Deliver Wins

1. Uncover common interests and goals
2. Ensure appropriate, well-timed wins
3. Employ reasonable resources

III

Turn Relationships into Productive Outcomes

First

Build Mutual Goals

1. Explore circles of influence
2. Evaluate resources and relationships
3. Mutually agree on three commitments

Second

Coach Stakeholders

1. List action steps and support materials
2. Examine resources and skills
3. Flex coaching styles

Three Relationship-Building Secrets

1. Be more curious.
2. Put the other person first, your needs second.
3. Uncover common interests, values, and goals.

Adapted from Marshall Howard & Associates' "Relationship Builders" © seminar, workshop, and consulting programs.

Relationship Builders

I. Capture the Right Stakeholder

Don't chase money. Identify and chase strong relationships.

The difference between receiving $250 from a donor or $25,000 comes down to one thing and one thing only: how well you execute the fundamentals.

Identify the Right Prospects

1. Profile four characteristics of your ideal stakeholder. List 2-3 major leadership roles he or she could fulfill.

2. Search for 25 to 35 profile matches. Examine past and existing donor pools, event participants, and personal contacts. Secure referrals.

3. Organize prospective stakeholders on a spreadsheet. Build fields that include the following: relationship holder's name, prospective stakeholder's name, title, company, and contact information, how referrer knows the prospect, and a grade ranking ("A" to "C").

4. Evaluate and rank each prospective stakeholder based on the following: accessibility, influence, financial potential, strength of relationship to the referrer, and match to the organization's mission.

5. Prioritize the first group of ten to fifteen people to be contacted.

Recruit Prospects to Become Stakeholders

1. Secure an introduction from each relationship holder. Prepare referrer talking points, and provide step-by-step coaching.

2. Make contact with the prospective stakeholder. Develop an initial picture about the person, ask one or two open-ended questions, set the appointment.

3. Conduct and lead a mission-focused, relationship building meeting. Ask questions, use time zones, share personal information.

4. Connect with each other, connect the prospective stakeholder to the mission, uncover the fit. Find common interests.

5. Test close. Ask open-ended questions, uncover and answer objections, bring meeting to a resolution.

Relationship Builders

II. Develop Win-Win Relationships

Once captured, stakeholders want wins, they want lots of them, and they want them continuously. If you don't continually uncover and deliver wins, someone else will. Without wins, supporters will pull up stakes and take their resources elsewhere.

The single most important thing in building a powerful relationship is to uncover things you and the stakeholder share. When two people see things in the world the same way, they feel they can trust each other. Little chemistry, not much in common. Lots of chemistry, a great deal in common.

Identify Stakeholder Wins

1. Develop a list of four possible personal wins and two possible business wins each stakeholder might want.

2. Get to know the stakeholder as a person first, donor second. Make the relationship the goal, develop a healthy curiosity, learn more about them, ask lots of questions, be more open and vulnerable.

3. Uncover common interests, shared ideas, values, and goals.

4. Build a written personal and professional stakeholder mosaic. Include information about a stakeholder's family, hobbies, achievements, nonprofit work, job experiences, business, and relationship to the mission.

5. Develop a series of four one-on-one, high-impact touches for each key stakeholder per year.

Continuously Deliver the Wins

1. Make the wins appropriate and well-timed. Ask direct, open-ended questions and listen carefully.

2. Uncover three reasons why the stakeholder became a supporter. Also uncover their expectations, how they see their leadership role with the organization, and their experiences with other nonprofits.

3. Uncover two to four possible wins a year for each key stakeholder.

4. Identify personal, organization, and volunteer resources that could be used to fulfill a stakeholder's wins.

5. Deliver, in a timely manner, at least two to three stakeholder wins each and every year.

Adapted from Marshall Howard & Associates' "Relationship Builders" © seminar, workshop, and consulting programs.

Relationship Builders

III. Turn Relationships into Productive Outcomes

It's not about being manipulative or tricky. It's the natural next step between two people who have a strong, win-win relationship. It's that connection that motivates them. They want to step up and help.

Most stakeholders have far more than money to offer.

Build Mutual Stakeholder Goals

1. Uncover a stakeholder's circles of personal and professional resources and relationships. List four to six that they can comfortably access and control.

2. Evaluate them. Select three or four that are needed, difficult to get, and would produce a big impact on the project, campaign, or mission.

3. Meet with the stakeholder. Ask some open-ended, test-close questions. Explore their willingness to share some of those resources with you and/or open doors to some of their relationships.

4. Mutually agree on two or three resources and/or relationships he or she will share. Formalize your agreement into a letter listing the commitments and thanking him or her for their support.

Coach Each Stakeholder

1. Develop a one-page written action plan and timeline, in partnership with the stakeholder, for each of their commitments.

2. Build a series of five steps needed to successfully fulfill each commitment. Assign to each step any required support materials.

3. Decide, with the stakeholder, what resources and whose resources will be used to accomplish each step. Also determine who is responsible for executing each of the steps.

4. Match the stakeholder's style. Flex your coaching to accommodate your stakeholder's personality, workstyle preferences, skills, and resources.

Adapted from Marshall Howard & Associates' "Relationship Builders" © seminar, workshop, and consulting programs.

Workshops & Training Seminars
Let's Have
Lunch
Together

Make these and many other stakeholder relationship strategies come alive at your next meeting or conference. Based on an extension of this book, Marshall Howard's high-energy keynote presentations, practical workshops, and interactive training seminars show participants how to easily integrate new, powerful relationship-building techniques into their busy schedules and development programs.

From flexible two-hour "lunch and learn" style workshops to half day through two day in-depth training seminars, high-impact relationship-building coaching can easily be a part of your next meeting agenda.

For over 24 years, Marshall Howard has taught staffs and boards, step-by-step, exactly how to go about building stronger connections. Marshall demystifies the art of great relationship-building. He'll remove the four biggest roadblocks, reveal the three relationship-building secrets, and deliver the practical how-to's – without an organization having to spend a ton of money, make massive changes, or take big risks.

Workshops & Training Seminars

Just like Oscar, recruit more leaders of influence and affluence, develop a powerful board and council, increase major and corporate giving and triple event income.

Let's Have Lunch Together workshops and seminars are tailored to an organization's challenges and venue. They're fun and interactive, with lots of takeaway tips that participants can immediately implement to get results.

Marshall Howard & Associates

Complementing Let's Have Lunch Together workshops and seminars, Marshall Howard and MH&A consultants provide targeted, one-on-one relationship development consulting to nonprofits nationwide.

Build a powerful Partnership Council with new, influential leaders, a more productive board or increase revenue from major giving, corporations, foundations, events, and campaigns. MH&A's 24 years of consulting experience helps organizations achieve more through the power of strong relationships with the right people.